FELIDAE ON THE ROAD

FELIDAE on the Road

AKIF PIRINÇCI

Translated from the German by
Anthea Bell

FOURTH ESTATE • LONDON

First published in Germany in 1994 by Goldmann Verlag

This translation first published in 1994 by
Fourth Estate Limited
289 Westbourne Grove
London W11 2QA

A catalogue record for this book is available from the British Library.

ISBN 1–85702–204–1

Typeset by Heronwood Press
Printed in Great Britain by The Bath Press Ltd

FOR CATS –
whether feline or human.

'I will not again curse the ground any more for man's sake; for the imagination of man's heart is evil from his youth; neither will I again smite any more every thing living, as I have done.'

GENESIS 8: 21. The Flood.

CHAPTER 1

They call it evolution. There's an invisible mechanism at work on this planet, they say, enabling the stronger to get stronger all the time and forcing the weaker into unconditional surrender. It's a law of nature, they say, and resistance is useless. The strong will survive and sooner or later the weak will be wiped off the face of the earth – that's what they call evolution.

But just who are all these weaklings doomed to perish? What are their names? What species do they belong to? Aren't they as much a part of this earth as the elect? Or are they simply anonymous, of unknown race, in-between stages on the way to final beatific perfection? Does the concept of nature conceal this melancholy fact? Is that the eternal law?

They call it evolution. I call it a crime.

Over the weeks that followed I was to learn a lot about this endless crime. But in the spring of this year, before it all began, I was lying on the yellow tapestry sofa in the living room without a care in the world. During the last few years the façade of the renovated old building had been overgrown by an ivy with delusions of grandeur, and it was gradually occupying the windows too. Consequently, only a few isolated sunbeams made their way like bright lances through the leaves and into the room, one of them falling on my head at that blessed moment of harmony like a spotlight. I lay majestically outstretched on the sofa, half dozing, half philosophising about the strange ways of the world, and I felt wonderfully comfortable. Life has certainly been good to me, I thought in all innocence. Here I lie, safe and warm, looking forward to stirring adventures this summer in the intricate setting of the gardens outside the back of the building.

This green oasis had long ceased to be a cosy garden-gnome sort of place and now displayed design trends of Babylonian complexity, with ornamental Japanese bridges surmounting artificial ecological habitats and paths paved by DIY enthusiasts in natural stone. In short, the former tenants – eternal students, folk who'd taken early retirement – had all been cast out of their idyllic surroundings, making way for people with peculiar-sounding double-barrelled surnames: people who sorted their rubbish for recycling and collected signatures on petitions against anything and everything. Although they wore battered straw hats to do their gardening, like half-starved Asians, you'd have been wrong to conclude that they were on the breadline. Far from it, in fact. It was just that their bloated complacency had taken strange forms and they'd moved into these old-fashioned buildings *en masse*. And *we* had moved in with them, of course. You're bound to see pictures of us in interior decorators' plans these days. We dot the i's and cross the t's of the good life.

So in fact I couldn't have done better for myself, even if my companion does spot fashionable trends with the same fervour as a City baboon following the fluctuations of the Dow Jones index.

There's really only one thing to be said for this so-called companion, whose name is Gustav Löbel: he doesn't eat the same sort of food as me, so I'm spared undignified squabbles about fair shares of whatever's in the bowl. The man is an eccentric mixture of Dumbo and Doctor Dolittle. (The Dolittle bit because he insists that his inconsequential soliloquies are 'conversations' with yours truly.) The mere sight of this hot-air balloon on legs doing perfectly ordinary jobs about the home is enough to make a cat laugh. But laughter soon turns to exasperation, because you'd never think a man of forty-nine weighing twenty stone could be such a fool. Well, did *you* ever meet anyone who could break his nose and burn the palms of both hands while cooking spaghetti? There's no call to go into the details of this incident. Just picture any scene you fancy from a slapstick cartoon film where everyday situations maliciously turn to a choreographic representation of chaos. With simple souls like Gustav, this can easily deteriorate into a case fit for *Casualty*. Up to a few years ago his main source of income was writing trashy novelettes for women's magazines under the name of Thalila, a pseudonym which may be considered sheer creative genius when you think of the tripe he concocted under it. The pattern of these daft stories was always the same: mother of eight mysteriously suffering from frigidity consults gynaecologist who is the spitting image of Bela Lugosi; gynaecologist drugs mother of eight on the pretext of conducting a thorough examination; gynaecologist repeatedly rapes her, gives her a sex change and then has the nerve to claim in court that he did it under the influence of laughing gas, thus getting off with probation and winning the Nobel Prize next day. Got all that quite clear, have you? To be fair to Gustav, it should be said that he was far from deriving any kind of satisfaction from this activity. He did it just to earn our bread. As a professor of Egyptology, in a career parallel to this deplorable scribbling, he had the reputation of being an authority in his field. It wasn't a very big reputation at first, but then he published work which created quite a sensation and his fame grew. Finally he was able to give up the newly-weds harassed by their mothers-in-law entirely, and devote himself exclusively to his beloved mummies and me.

Which doesn't mean that our relationship became any

easier. Relieved of the nagging anxiety as to whether the fee for the trash he'd just cobbled together would cover the next electricity bill, he had so much extra leisure time that he took to treating me like a New Age father persuaded, by dint of a cocktail of tax loopholes and obscure appeals from the feminist front line, to abandon a good career and try the maternal role for size. His earlier fits of solicitude had often made me wonder why on earth he ever got me instead of a comfort blanket. But now all the baby talk and the tempting offers of increasingly exquisite delicacies were really getting me down. A substitute, that's what I was, just a love substitute for this failure who knew nothing about the female form except from tedious nudist videos, and nothing about the female psyche except from those magazines he used to write for. A love substitute for a hermit whose odd life-style led him to indulge in some very peculiar rituals – like the irritating fuss he made over his thousands of pipes and brands of tobacco – and who ended every day with at least two bottles of French red wine, since the night hours showed him to himself in a particularly painful light. A substitute for children never conceived and friends who never knocked on his door.

Almost bald, afflicted with the worst stoop in orthopaedic history and an expression not unlike that of a melancholy hippopotamus going through the menopause, this exponent of petting as terrorism was getting to be more and more of a burden to me since he'd stopped providing escapist stories for sexually harassed secretaries. I've no objection to grooming in moderation, but the constant feeling that I was merely a compensation for an old professor's failures in life both saddened and irritated me. At this point you may well ask why, with so much smother-love lavished on me, I didn't just pack my things one night and move in with the busy yuppie a few doors up the road. All he'd have required of me would be to sit decoratively on his Le Corbusier chaise-longue during the champagne parties he threw.

Well, there weren't many reasons for me to stay, but those there were carried weight. First and foremost, the question of cultural standards. In human terms Gustav might be a total idiot, but his intellectual horizons were open to culture and scholarship, even philosophy on occasion, although unlike me he had never explored the gloomy depths of the likes of Schopenhauer. Of course there are others of my kind who are smitten with such things, but I well remember the delight I felt as a child when I sat on his shoulder, looking at the books he was reading until I had taught myself to read too and was infected by the same sweet plague. And I remember our orgies of Mahler and Wagner on his old Dual record player as we sat by the fire on cold winter evenings. Strictly speaking, then, it was a combination of intellectual compatibility and habit that bound us together. We both revered the intellectual achievements of civilisation, and we both hated all the ugliness daily created outside our four walls by devils in many forms. Habit, of course, can also mean stagnation. Yet who would seriously deny that once youth is over, any inclination to philistinism will attack every cell of a person's being like a tenacious virus?

So was there anything else to justify my staying with this Oliver Hardy of the educated classes? Love, maybe? Hm, well, it's difficult to give a straightforward answer to that. Think of those coy little maxims beginning 'Love is . . . ', going on with the alleged evidence in remarks like ' . . . when you can laugh all the same!' and printing a cartoon underneath showing a naked little couple holding hands in a nauseatingly sweet pose. I don't believe you can explain the phenomenon of love that way. Love's more like a constant flow of lava beneath the earth's crust; we are unaware of it until it suddenly erupts from volcanoes long believed extinct, surprising us with its unimaginable power. But I'm straying into metaphors, and I don't know if they really cast light on the curious relationship between me and my 'master' Gustav.

Anyway, this part of my story is not the place for sentimental analyses of love in an old couple rather the worse for wear like Gustav and me.

In general love doesn't turn out as expected. That's life. Had I known, that memorable afternoon, of the change about to come over my life in the next few seconds, I doubt if I'd have been indulging in critical reflections on Gustav, I'd have been wallowing in pure nostalgia. Oh yes, I was going to miss my simple-minded friend. Indeed, I was going to find I loved him so much I'd willingly have signed a ten-year contract to be the victim of his petting. For the one thing sure to bring a living creature endowed with reason to his senses is the loss of those comforts he's acquired over the course of time. In short, I didn't know when I was well off.

Before I come to this radical watershed in my life, let me make a few last remarks about the changes that had imperceptibly been made to the paradise described above. For all I was so well off, a sensitive spirit like mine couldn't help being aware of an alteration in the urban climate dating some way back. I'd heard with increasing frequency of burglaries in our part of town, mindless acts of violence even in the posh villa where the respected local dentist lived. Shabbily dressed figures in a sozzled condition, carrying plastic bags, prowled around our comfortable fortresses, knocking on our perfect replicas of original walnut doors and begging. And I hate to think what they did to members of my own kind if they could get their hands on us, there being good reason to suppose that the only how-to manuals they ever read had such tempting titles as *How to Cook Domestic Pets*.

Another nuisance stemmed from the inorganic kingdom. It isn't true that rabbits breed faster than anything else in the world. In point of fecundity, monsters made of steel and plastic overtook rabbits ages ago. By now it was practically impossible to do as you could in the old days – take a pleasant stroll round the neighbourhood, have a nice little dust-up with Bigmouth Tom over the road here, do your bit towards the preservation of ancient monuments there with some environmentally friendly spraying – without constantly running the risk of being suddenly chosen by Fate as an up-to-date radiator mascot for a car, only not on the radiator but lower down.

I was obviously not the only one struck by this decline in the quality of life. Those who caused it had noticed too, and the word 'country', a word full of promise, was being bandied about more and more insistently. Escape from the city, that was the idea. People got all excited by TV cereal ads showing country life in hues of the ripest golden corn as a kind of never-ending picnic with at least eight sunrises a day, ditto sunsets. Even I was slowly falling for such illusions. In my mind's eye, I already saw myself roaming fertile meadows at crack of dawn, sitting on the river bank methodically decimating stocks of some indefinable kind of fish, and washing them down with a huge bowl of milk taken from the cow by Gustav's own hands. There was nothing on my imaginary Disneyland farm but fresh air, fresh eggs from birds which probably nested right on the chimneys of our farmhouse, and eternally fresh young females in a state of nymphomania – no Mickey Mice, though, because eating them made me feel sick even in dreams. I used these fantasies to shield myself from the horror stories that reached me from the wicked city, tales of brothers and sisters there and witty folk who thought it amusing to stick iron bars up their arses.

'Of its very nature, desire means pain: its fulfilment quickly breeds satiety; the goal was only apparent, and possession of it deprives it of its attraction. Desire and need will reappear in a new guise, or if not, then desolation, emptiness and tedium will follow, and to contend with those is as hard as to contend with want.' Well, Schopenhauer was dead wrong about that! Because when my desire to wave goodbye to city life was finally granted, desolation, emptiness and tedium were not what followed at all. Sheer horror, that was what followed, so there! This is the true story of a dream which turned to a nightmare . . .

Sleep, which contrary to appearances is of poorer quality in me than in humans,[1] had passed like a sultry wind lulling you with pleasant warmth on the one hand, threatening to smother you gently on the other. Muddled thoughts about my little world and the problems that loomed so large in it had disturbed my nap, distilling from it a sour, hung-over and compulsively pessimistic feeling, as sleeping in the day usually does. I felt rested, all the same, and fit to risk a first glance at the waking world. Maybe it would be a good idea to go straight to the fridge now, dig the claws of my left paw into the white rubber seal, walk slowly backwards in order to open the door, and then tuck into a nice fresh stick of Italian salami. The fridge-opening trick can never be explained too often; many of my colleagues will scratch or tear at the door excitedly in their greed, forgetting that the muscle power of a small paw won't work as an Open Sesame on something so firmly shut. Success depends on simply using your claws as a grappling hook, your whole body as a traction engine, and your paw to transfer the tractive power. Oh yes, and don't forget to slam the door shut afterwards.

So I opened my eyes.

I saw a face, right in front of my nose. Sometimes sleep has a nasty way of making you believe you've woken up while in fact you're still in the imaginary world of dreamland. That's what I thought had happened now. Because what I saw didn't belong in the world of my own experience, or in a world of which I wanted to have any experience either. I am often accused of comparing people with colourful figures of pop culture, particularly film stars, thereby giving a distorted and ultimately inaccurate idea of the person I'm describing. OK, I promise to mend my ways – but let me make one last reference to Hollywood, because this time it really does hit the nail on the head. The face of the woman leaning over me, some thirty centimetres away, was a replica of the actress Joan Crawford's. Her eyebrows were thick black arcs like the diva's, looming menacingly over eyelashes lengthened to infinity with mascara and eyes the size of ping-pong balls. Her angular chin was obviously designed in a heavy machinery engineering workshop, but the focal point of her whole face was her mouth, painted fire-engine red. The lip pencil had made her lips almost twice their real size, giving her the look of a jet bomber with a fearsome shark's mouth painted on the nose by bored soldiers. The only difference between her and the film star was her hair, which was definitely greying, but like the original model's it was set as if in concrete by tornadoes of hair-spray.

She wasn't looking at me, she was sort of glittering at me, and I felt as if her cold grey eyes were blasting me with a thousand lightning flashes. With an expression of condescension, even distaste, as if wondering what to do about me, she observed my incredulous reactions the way a cheetah observes an antelope calf wedged tight among rocks. It gradually dawned on me that this grotesque stranger, who could easily have featured as a goddess screeching for revenge in some ancient opera, was perfectly real. And with prophetic certainty, I knew at once that she was going to shake the very foundations of my own future reality. The good old times were over. Here came the bad.

Where was Gustav? What had happened? Who in hell was this monstrous nicotine-stained mouth surrounded by a small quantity of woman and apparently drenched in some unspeakable Arabian perfume for old ladies? Was she a witch hypnotising me with a view to skinning me later, to make herself a smart forties-style hat? While all these impressions plunged me into wild confusion, making the hairs on my back rise and my whiskers vibrate, she shook her head slightly and disapprovingly, and delivered herself of the fateful words:

'He's moulting!'

That was it. The signal. It confirmed – if I needed any confirmation – all my fears and forebodings about this snaky character. It was like the shadow of the approaching priest falling on the poor sod in the condemned cell. However, it was no use staying there frozen rigid in a state of shock and desperation; I had to nip this in the bud and add a little something extra to the enemy's first impressions of me. It was true, your old friend Francis *was* moulting a bit. But that was as nothing to the spectacular hair loss she was about to sustain.

Functioning like a steel catapult, my powerful hind legs launched me off the sofa and right into her face. She acted as if she'd been struck by a cannon ball and staggered back, screeching. I'd expected the skin of her face to come off in flakes, considering its owner's age, but I was extremely surprised, and delighted, to find that the claws of both my forepaws sank into her as easily as if they'd been the prongs of a large chrome fork, raising her shrill screams by several satisfying decibels. Then she was kind enough to tip her head back too, so now I was standing four-square on her face, in a position to start on the real plastic surgery.

However, my adversary knew a thing or two as well. Whether in panic reaction, or because she'd learnt the grips as part of her training to be an all-in mud wrestler, she instantly grabbed me by both flanks, squeezed my ribs together and tried to squash the life out of me. But I slipped nimbly out of her fingers, got tangled up in her sticky coiffure, hissing, and shredded it like a cotton gin gone crazy. As the blood began to flow, I saw Gustav out of the corner of one eye. He was standing in the doorway, in imminent danger of a choking fit, waving his arms helplessly in the air. His flushed face, his eyes wide with terror and the silent scream issuing from his mouth really got on my wick. Apparently his alarm wasn't for me at all. Good heavens above, it wasn't as if I was remodelling his dear old mother's head!

The witch did the only thing she could in this chaotic situation: she fell backwards with a gurgling cry for help, demanding the police, the fire brigade, and a decision by the UN Security Council in favour of military intervention. Myself, I was so confused I simply wanted to do a runner and cool down a bit. So I let go of the lady, who had theatrically fainted away at what, when you stopped to think of it, was a suspiciously convenient moment, and raced for the underpass formed by my traumatised companion's legs planted on the floor wide apart. All I had to do after that was turn sharp left at the doorway into the corridor, and then I could get out of the flat through the front door. I hoped it was open.

We're probably the best accelerators in the world. In proportion to body size and weight, even the smartest Ferrari can't compete. So I got off to a flying start which made everything moving around me seem to be in extremely slow motion. But flashes of inspiration are known to move even faster than we do. And during the millisecond it took me to reach Gustav's legs, a couple of revealing snapshots from the very recent past flashed into my mind. The scales fell from my eyes . . .

The witch wasn't Gustav's mother. Nor was she the judge of the Claw of the Year contest come to present me with a cup. Memories, memories, memories . . . Hadn't my poor lonely friend come home from the wine bar in the next street at a most unchristian time of night a few weeks ago, all boozed up, warbling a slushy waltz to himself at inconsiderately loud volume and of course horribly out of tune – and guess what, hadn't he been reeking of some heavy, nauseating perfume? He seldom went to the wine bar at all in the usual way, and when he did he was always back before midnight, because drinking on your own is no fun. This time, moreover, he'd strutted round the whole flat in a very odd way, sort of impassioned and prancing about in imitation of a prima ballerina. In view of his tubby figure, this performance had me rolling in the aisles. Before he collapsed into bed and fell asleep babbling blissfully, like a baby doped with morphine, he undressed in the manner of a megalomaniac baron, puffing out his chest and flinging his shirt, his trousers and even his underwear all round the room (his underpants landed on the plaster cast of Nefertiti). I put this conduct down to the demon drink, although Gustav had never sunk to quite this level before.

And over the next few weeks, hadn't he spent hours sitting in his study with a faraway look in his eyes, writing letters on hand-made paper to the accompaniment of great yearning sighs? I should have asked myself who those letters were to. Because after putting them in their envelopes he licked the gummed strip as worshipfully as if he were trying to breathe life into them. And there'd been phone calls, oh yes! But as usual I'd been careful not to listen, since his infuriating habit of uttering meaningless exclamations of 'Really?' and 'You don't say!' the whole time during phone calls brought me to the brink of murder. All the same, my suspicions should have been aroused by the fact that during some of these conversations his voice performed acrobatics which changed his usual growl into a ridiculously soppy, velvety tone, while he dwelt ominously on words like 'you' and 'we'. And to crown my ignorance, I should mention the most striking change of all: Gustav's brand-new wardrobe. I'd mistakenly ascribed this to his advancing senility, which I first noticed coming on in 1985. Sometimes it was a canary-yellow summer suit, sometimes silk shirts with full sleeves – in themselves, of course, the last word in bad taste, but omitting to notice these clues was striking evidence of the failure of my famous analytical capacities.

Well, we really were up the creek now! The old fool was in

love! And not content with that, he was even letting this tart desecrate the temple of what had once seemed our eternal partnership! Jealous, me? Not a bit of it! At that bleak moment, however, I realised that things would never be the same between us again.

Gustav made a desperate effort to catch me as I slipped past through his legs. It can't have been a serious attempt, since his gigantic paunch, guaranteed to act as a lifebelt and keep him above water in any shipwreck, made him incapable of swift reactions. The thought: 'I've done it!' shot through my head before I turned the corner and kept right on going – kept right on going, sad to say, for ever and ever.

The last thing I saw after that was a shining mountain. It consisted of metal suitcases stacked on top of each other and covered with stickers saying things like 'Kennedy Airport' and 'Sydney', suggestive of wide cosmopolitan experience. They reflected the sunlight flooding in from the study. So that was it! This wasn't just a one-off visit to Romeo's pad, oh no, Juliet was about to take the whole place over. But I had no time to explode with anger. My flight reflex and my disillusionment had wound me up to such an amazing speed that I could have smashed my way right through a wall at that suicidal tempo, had a wall suddenly appeared in front of me. It's one thing to think up fantastic comparisons, something else entirely to face them when they turn real. Because the wall had in fact been there for quite some time, in the shape of that mountain of suitcases. I didn't even try to slam the brakes on, and before I could work out further the meaning of this turn Fate had taken, my skull collided full tilt with the heftiest of the suitcases, which was standing up lengthwise. It looked more like a tombstone than a suitcase, such was my brain's last conscious thought: my own tombstone with a particularly cogent comment by Schopenhauer carved on it: 'The truth is that we are meant to be miserable – and miserable we are!'

CHAPTER 2

I should have lingered in my faint, because no state of unconsciousness, however profound, can be worse than the sudden disruption of all a person's cherished daily routines. And nothing can do more devastating damage than a female descending like a biblical plague on the life of a confirmed bachelor, a life which you could only have described as blissful. To put it as a politician would, the alliance between Gustav and me, founded on liberty, equality and fraternity but even more on cosy congeniality, was being shattered by a totalitarian usurper employing all the relevant methods of administrative terrorism. Under this new rule of terror, the slightest misdemeanour was mercilessly punished. The real tragedy of it, however, was the fact that my companion, having reached the absolute nadir of debility, was not in a state to put up much resistance.

No sooner had I come round again – and I was surprised to find the two of them had put me on the bed in the bedroom instead of chucking me straight in the dustbin – no sooner had I come round than I heard, as if from distant battlefields, our new generalissima in the process of seizing power. Hers was a really low-down strategy. She thought everything was wonderful, just wonderful – I heard words to that effect in tones suggesting the lengthy application of a goods train's emergency brakes – but hadn't Gustav noticed how sterile those white-painted walls made the flat look? Just like a man! No notion of the psychosomatic interaction of wall colour with personal well-being. Herself, she could never bear to live in a place that wasn't painted apricot-pink. As for the replica of a Babylonian frieze ornamented with gold leaf on the wall – good heavens, were we living in a museum? A Lichtenstein might be expensive, but still, it would be an investment. Of course tastes differed, but the study really had all the charm of a Calcutta pawnshop. To call it chaotic was too kind a description. Gustav had better go straight into town and buy a stack of files so that she could organise his papers. If he thought she'd failed to notice the half-eaten chop in the sink, he was wrong. And did he know that eating meat could actually *kill* a person? Well, diet wasn't the only thing about to change around here. And as for that br – that animal, even living creatures of 'extremely low intelligence' should be trained to do certain things. No, no, she didn't bear a grudge because of the contretemps just now, but after all Gustav wasn't Tarzan, still less was she Jane, and she had no intention of spending the rest of her life as some kind of Mother Teresa of domestic pets. To be honest, she really preferred dogs . . .

Was anything more needed to show me that my days in the Garden of Eden were numbered? The answer was obviously yes. For the perception of misfortune usually goes hand in hand with lazy compromise; the mammalian brain seems to be so constructed as to make the best of even the most hopeless situation. At such times you tend to play the optimistic clown, even when you'd need potatoes instead of eyes not to notice you were in deep trouble. You start deceiving yourself and coming to terms with disaster. And that's what I did too. Things are never as bad as they seem, I thought – a surprising lapse into the sententious which was the first step towards lowering my standards. I even went to the trouble of trying to put myself in *her* emotional situation, although robot warriors don't have one. A woman is not a man, I told myself with grim logic, and she'd be a pretty poor representative of her sex if she didn't drag her fool of a companion into the wonderful world of flowers on the dining table, Easter walks together, and the nagging about clothes and haircuts that ends only in the grave. Admittedly Gustav wasn't a man in his twenties, assailed by turbulent hormones, leading a cave-man life in student digs surrounded by foil ready-meal trays and the poisonous gases from his dirty socks. Over the years, however, despite the high cultural level of our life together, a certain lack-lustre element had crept in. It frequently does when an all-male society gets set in its ways. Wouldn't the hand of a loving woman bring a little freshness and sunshine into a pedestrian existence, which might function smoothly but was gradually fossilising, what with all the rituals of the bachelor life? I asked myself that question in all seriousness . . . and next moment I yelled back the answer: Nooooooo! Good heavens above, was the curse this tarted-up cow – I bet she used mouth spray – was the curse this silly old moo had laid on my poor friend affecting me too? How come I was regarding a sour old dragon who obviously wanted me up in front of a firing squad as a self-sacrificing newly-wed bride?

Over the next few days my fears were to be confirmed, indeed far exceeded. Here are some extracts from the wrathful diary I kept in my mind, reproduced by kind permission of my photographic memory.

Day 1

Didn't sleep a wink all night. Horrible woman keeps making noises in her sleep. Noises like squeals of torment from King Kong's cage. Wondered if grotesque parody of snoring was just to annoy me. Came to no conclusion. Stupid man snores too. His version, however, more like the comfortable burping of grizzly bears in hibernation; have always found something soothing, even beneficial to quality of sleep, about it. Now, however, two kinds of snoring united in frightful duet, symphony of horror fit to rival rutting cries of aurochs.

Horrible woman is fanatical early riser – sign of horrible people in general. The moment her old red alarm clock starts clattering, like Satan calling his followers to deeds of sin, woman sits bolt upright in bed. Waking process therefore noisy too. Woman's figure not bad, but general appearance rather skinny. Inadequate concealment of wreckage left by innumerable crash diets. Makes stupid man get up early too and have breakfast with her. Breakfast celebrated with as much ceremony as Ascension Day Mass in the Vatican. Takes about as long too. Stupid man goes to endless trouble to seem awake. Well, no choice, has he? Non-stop chatter inflicted on us by Archaeopteryx rules out morning meditation anyway.

In melancholy mood, indulge in memories. Before era of dark power, day began with loving customs, aforesaid love able to thrive only when partners mutually respect and inspire each other. First, opening my tin of food, frying a few bits of liver, addition of liver to my dish, or maybe fish with a beaten egg in a separate saucer. Fragrance of freshly brewed coffee filling our cosy kitchen. During Gustav's lavish breakfast, all kinds of delicious titbits jumping off the table *entirely of their own accord,* straight into my waiting mouth. Those were the days! Days of joy and tenderness. But now . . . Had to shout several times in very undignified manner to attract attention. Either horrible woman's hypnotic power causing dereliction of duty, or he daren't make me centre of his life as before, since consequence would be criminal jealousy. If latter supposition correct, have not only been deceived in him for years, have also been deceiving myself. Which is much, much sadder.

A heart is breaking . . .

Day 2
Stupid man out at work all day, so had chance to observe horrible woman in private. Feel like Einstein of anthropology, since all my hypotheses dead right. Woman may make self out fanatical vegetarian (don't ask me why; woman hates animals even more than her wrinkles, misuses every variety of fruit and vegetable on God's earth as face masks to do away with those). However, caught her ordering five kebab skewers from snack delivery service at lunch-time, devouring same with bestial greed of cannibal. Noticed me watching; was so cross threw huge can of hair-spray at me.

Woman also chocaholic. OK, spends hours preparing pygmy-sized dishes to strict calorie counts, but also frequently subject to attacks of acute sugar addiction. Chocolate bars concealed in cunning hiding-places all over flat, like mines, or no, more like secret drinker's treasured supplies. Woman makes straight for hidden chocolate if above-mentioned attacks come over her. Have to hand it to her powers of memory; even dog of genius couldn't remember that many buried bones. Expression on woman's face as fangs sink into poor innocent chocolate in no way inferior to grimaces during kebab orgies.

No end to woman's repellent habits: serious historians now know telephone invented especially for human female. Almost erotic relationship of women in general to that great achievement in communications technology offers fruitful field of study to anthropologists. Real world-beaters, however, to be found among research subjects as a whole. Horrible woman streets ahead of all rivals. Sure bet for gold medal in competitive rabbiting on. Couldn't easily be beaten at random picking of numbers from address book – result of pure boredom – or amazing idiocy of conversation then conducted, idiocy being proportionate to length. During said conversations, everyday incidents like purchase of plastic earclips at very reasonable price analysed in their every metaphysical aspect, likewise harmless encounters with men blown up into astounding Arthurian sagas. Long-suffering man who pays phone bill, proper Charlie in my view, needs to have brought off business *coup* of his life today. One of many conversations, lasted over an hour, was with girlfriend in Florida. All at stupid man's expense. And stupid is the word.

Murderous plans taking shape in mind . . .

Day 3

Made two observations; said observations flatly contradict each other. Surreptitious rustling and gurgling in night, made me think Creator inflicting ghosts on us as well as that beast, as if she wasn't enough. Guessed wrong. Man and woman making love! Jumped straight up on bedroom chest of drawers to make close observations of unique phenomenon. In light of stupid man's bizarre anatomy, process not without problems. Was flabbergasted: process apparently worked perfectly well, though no detailed study possible because duvet hiding much from view. Main points, however, as follows: 1. Judging by unrealistic sexy noises, horrible woman simulating deep feeling throughout. Faked orgasm verging on ludicrous. Genuine version of similar salvo of moans possibly heard on occasion by Richard Gere but never by stupid man, you bet your life. 2. Though fascinated by entire show, had good reason to fear stupid man might suffer heart attack any minute. Several times previously had been obliged to witness grunting of *Homo masculinus* during sexual act (when stupid man, using remote control, inadvertently switched to down-market commercial channels), so was to some extent familiar with subject. But euphoric wheezing emitted by globular mound under duvet more reminiscent of loud whimpering of patient on operating table when medical staff going easy on anaesthetic. Could hardly tell whether sounds of pain or pleasure predominant during whole show.

Revolting business, all things considered, even if supposed to be love! How nonchalantly, by comparison, my own kind propagates the species! But *they* never learn! Got no thanks for purely scientific curiosity but to come under fire from horrible woman again. Woman became aware of my interested observation of unilateral climax, screeched, grabbed chrome tissue-box holder, slung chrome holder at me with muscular force of doped female Romanian shot-putter. Missed again, though got closer than last time; no damage except to antique mirror on chest of drawers behind me. Hysterical little idiot!

Next morning, totally different programme. Talk about incongruity between loving vows of a spring night and disillusionment of everyday life! Anyway, woman's claims on my own territory becoming clearer and clearer. Stupid man seems to be gradually realising has made mistake of life – but alas, too late! Third World War broke out during breakfast discussion. She absolutely determined to put own 'ideas' about furnishings, financial investments and life-style into practice, no quarter shown. Apparently woman was once interior decorator. Also psychologist. Also artist. Also . . . well, don't ask me what woman is now! Divorcee, probably. In same shrill voice as always scares off dear little birdies in garden just as yours truly about to spring, stupid man told to renovate entire flat from top to bottom to suit her taste. When man made some objections – man's degenerate cells seem to retain a few male hormones after all – screeching became howling hurricane threatening to sweep us away. Naturally woman has no armaments to atomise him, for instance rocket launcher or such-like, so reached for most reliable weapon of her own kind, started shedding tears. Man instantly defended self and signed own death sentence in imaginary treaty as mentally concluded by such couples: stupid sucker said would do everything, but everything woman wanted if woman would only stop that miserable weeping. Since bawling working so well, woman speedily rattled off more wishes in between heavy sigh and next fit of sobbing: wish list began, oddly, with asking man to throw away old white cotton underpants and please, please buy some of the trendy coloured sort. Really, if not all so sad would be riotously funny. But laughter dies in my throat when I wonder what part allotted to me in woman's diabolical game. Because after cooked-up reconciliation, ending with both of them thoughtfully eating boiled eggs (and instructions from woman for man to decapitate egg with clean knife-cut in future instead of peeling shell off top), woman turned head to me, very slowly, with kind of bittersweet smile executioner might give principal actor in drama. Suddenly saw that had lost battle ages ago, and must leave Promised Land for ever.

End of diary.

Or maybe not; one more thing. What was her name? I hardly like to tell you, but I must, I must: it was Francesca!

The thing that finally set me off on my travels was a wicked lie. While Gustav and that – that *person* – were throwing out items of furniture to go to the tip, and doing all kinds of other daft things with a view to turning the whole place upside down, I kept hearing her utter the mysterious words: 'Those nuts must go!' At first I could make nothing whatever of this; least of all could I see any connection with myself. As far as I knew Gustav never ate nuts, and I certainly didn't. So what nuts did she mean? Repeated with ever-increasing frequency, the remark began assuming disturbing dimensions when I realised that it was always made when I was around. And things became downright scary when she slowly but surely went on to wrinkling her upper lip, glaring accusingly at me, theatrically pretending to detect some disgusting smell in the air and sighing in an affected way, 'Dear me, those nuts must go!' The mystery of the nuts preoccupied me more than ever as the connection between 'nuts' and yours truly became clearer with every passing day. So during a quiet moment when they were both out of the house, I sat on the side of the bathroom basin, inspected myself in the mirror, and thought with all the keen powers of my mind. I was looking for something nut-like about myself, or more precisely, something nuts-like, because she always mentioned these nuts in the plural. No, my reflection showed nothing, or at least nothing like nuts. Unless perhaps . . . oh no, that was too far-fetched – it was absurd, ridiculous, more than ridiculous, it was . . .[2]

I saw them there in the mirror, dangling between my thighs like sacred fruits in the Elysian Fields, like revelations of power and glory, my nuts, those engines of procreation the good Lord gave me! At the same time, as if in a double exposure, I saw the vision of a surgeon emerge from this impressive still life, but a surgeon with a sinister difference, holding a barber's instrument – a cut-throat razor! In terrifying parody of his profession, he wore a scarlet coat, and the cap and mask which made his face unrecognisable were the colour of blood too. This horrific figure loomed closer and closer without actually stepping forward until its face filled the entire mirror. My breath faltered. Suddenly the hand holding the sharp blade rose and tore the mask from the face. Jesus Christ and Mary Magdalene! I saw Francesca, her eyes boring into my innocent soul like icicles fired from a harpoon. That witch, that horrible woman, that brute was after my nuts!

Shocked by this nightmare vision, I jumped off the side of the basin and ran into the living room, which was bathed in sunlight. I got up on my beloved tapestry sofa, which wasn't due for removal on Francesca's orders until some time in the next few days, and shook myself hard to clear my head. As I made myself comfortable on the cushions, my heart thumping wildly, I started working out the way she was probably trying to justify such a barbaric mutilation to Gustav. Of course I knew how many beans make five: I was well aware that some ninety per cent of my colleagues went around without any nuts to their name. After the op their faces usually wore the ecstatic expression peculiar to the ascetic disciples of a fraudulent Indian guru who has managed to have it all ways by making his home a brothel. They seemed to have lost more than their testicles; somehow or other they had lost their zing, their love of adventure, and even worse, they'd lost heart. Despite that, they sometimes became furiously aggressive for no obvious reason, as if they hadn't noticed their sad loss until they peed and saw their reflection in the puddle of piss. Experience told me, however, that all they did with their lives was sit on walls and window-sills mourning the past like pensioned-off border guards, keeping an eye on their territories but otherwise letting the world go by. If a queen on call ever did come their way by mistake and rolled, wailing sexily, before their dull eyes, they'd get all excited in a childish way, as if suddenly hearing echoes of a cry, long mute, from dark primeval times. I don't want to attract a storm of indignant protest with this description of misery, so let me add, with scrupulous honesty, that there may be exceptions among my comrades who've lost their crown jewels. With respect, however, the amputation of one's sexual organs is not to be compared with the extraction of a rotten tooth.

So what was her nefarious plan? Just what cunning ruse did the witch have in mind to make Gustav imprison his beloved Francis in a basket and cart him off to the vet who, for a princely fee, would part him and his nuts for ever? The most unkindest cut of all, literally. Because so far my nuts had never bothered Gustav himself. Far from it: he rather liked to see me doing my bit out in the gardens to prevent the extinction of the species, probably as compensation for his own failure in the reproductive sphere. The answer was simple. Francesca had obviously been feeding the idiot that old line about the likes of me leaving liquid stink-bombs round the flat when in amorous mood. And since in fact there wasn't any stink, she must have suggested that there was something wrong with his sense of smell while extolling the unusual sensitivity of her own. The deduction was as logical as 1 + 1 = 2: off with his nuts!

Reflecting on this gloomy prospect, I nodded off. A leaden slumber overcame me, and by the time I woke up night had fallen. I felt as if I'd only just escaped from a defective pressure chamber. At first I didn't think I could even move the tip of my tail, all my limbs were so numb. It was only with difficulty that I shook off my paralysis, got to my feet and arched my back more stiffly than ever before in my entire career. Meanwhile, a spring shower had begun outside. The patter of the rain was soothing. Then it all came back to me, and I took a panic-stricken look between my legs. It was so dark in the room that I couldn't spot my crown jewels straight away, and for a fraction of a second I thought I was going crazy. But then I felt their warmth, their weight, their whole regal splendour, and I pulled myself together again.

The hands of the clock on the wall stood at twenty past three. That afternoon's terrible experiences had obviously put me out like a light, so that I hadn't heard the lovers coming home or even felt hungry for supper. Late as it was, however, I heard voices in the bedroom. With as little sound as a scarf dropped on the floor, I jumped off the sofa and approached the bedroom door. Then I stood outside and listened. It was not a quarrel going on in there, more the spooky kind of conference that takes place between victor and vanquished at the end of a war. They'd just reached an interesting section of the negotiations, apparently the last, dealing with the pros and cons of neutering domestic pets. The victorious power was going over the advantages of this 'therapeutic treatment' once more, not to convince the vanquished but because running through the positions stated before battle commenced is part of the political ritual. Gustav had to accept the outcome whether he liked it or not. She was pouring out all the confused tripe you'll find in every well-intentioned book about our species. First, it's all for our own good; you might think it was *only* as a side effect that the result left humans with a sparkling clean home and spared them hours of lustful nocturnal caterwauling and the distasteful business of drowning our unwanted progeny in the bath. Such duplicity almost made me throw up. Gustav, lying there in the dark like Billy Bunter on his deathbed, wearily uttered an occasional *if* and *but* like responses in a litany, whereupon Francesca the Snow Queen smothered his misgivings with a brand-new knock-out argument. Her visions went even further: far in the future she saw a wonderful New World in which my claws would be amputated so as to preserve the beautiful furniture they'd just ordered from suffering ugly scratch marks.[3] Good heavens, what tortures were yet in store for me?

I have to admit that I wouldn't have set out on my travels, or not that night anyway, if Gustav had had the decency to put up any kind of serious resistance – if he'd kept the matter open for at least a little longer. After all, we'd been faithful friends for years, ever since my birth, in fact. We'd come through many difficult times and celebrated many a happy event together. How about love . . . was there no love left in this dark world? No trust? Once upon a time Gustav had *really and truly* loved me more than anything else . . .

But before they cuddled up and – this you will hardly believe – before they started making 'love' in their own disgusting way after discussing this very subject, he just said, 'All right' and 'I'll take him in tomorrow.' 'Traitor!' I felt like screeching. 'You double-crossing two-timing traitor!' But I didn't. Why not? Well, what would you expect of creatures – never mind the individual exceptions – who will train dogs to tear each other apart, who put rings through the sensitive noses of bears and tug them about by those rings to the wild applause of the crowd, and who regard the public butchering of some poor bull as the peak of virility? Would you expect trust? Pity? Respect? Even the devil keeps his pacts signed in blood. To date, however, man hasn't honoured a single clause in the contract we made with him back in primeval times when he depended on us for everything. Or to call upon my good old teacher Schopenhauer for another quotation: 'Man is a fierce wild animal at heart. We know that animal only in the tamed condition of restraint known as civilisation, and so the occasional outbreaks of its true nature horrify us. But wherever, whenever the padlock and chain of law and order fall away and anarchy sets in, then we see what man is.' And that's not the only time, I might add.

I turned away from the two wild animals who were copulating again, unmoved by the prospect of their small friend's mutilation, ran across the kitchen and the bathroom and jumped up on the window-sill. Before me stretched the dark gardens, wet with rain, like a sinister threat. Behind me lay what in spite of occasional vexations had once seemed the best of all possible worlds. I would have liked to die in that world when my hour came. Faded pictures which I thought I'd eradicated from the memory centres of my brain rose before my mind's eye, like flowers from an up-ended cornucopia, accompanied by sweet hurdy-gurdy music. I went back over our happy days in my mind, including that episode when I laid the first mouse I ever caught on Gustav's desk as a kind of sacrificial lamb, out of pure respect. It was only half eaten, too. Yes, there had been sad times as well. But hadn't I been the ideal therapy for him, snuggling under the bedclothes in the dark of night and soaking up his tears in my fur? Hadn't he always introduced me to his few friends as his 'son'? He used to make out it was a joke, but he really meant it in all seriousness. What evil spell had so bewitched my 'father' that his heart had suddenly turned to granite?

Tears came into my eyes, ran down my nose and dripped off my chin. The patter of the rain provided a melancholy accompaniment to my bleak mood, and I suddenly saw, with crystal clarity, all I'd have to give up if I left home now. Obviously I couldn't cast about for a new home anywhere in the neighbourhood, because Gustav would be sure to get a search operation going in the morning. No, I must go far, far away, even leave town, go where Missing notices tacked to tree-trunks and ads in the Lost and Found columns of newspapers wouldn't work. Well, asked the optimist in my head (not a fellow who inspires a lot of confidence), haven't you been feeling very keen on the country life recently? Here's your chance. It was hard to say if he meant it seriously or if he was stifling roars of laughter. I hope you realise, said the pessimist in me, that you'd have to accept a few alterations to your diet, to put it mildly? Particularly where quantity of food is concerned – always supposing you find any food at all. This pessimist made a deep impression on me – yet there was something apathetic, even lethargic about him, as if he'd really rather let things slide.

Before the problem could be flogged to death in discussion yet again, I saw the vision of that menacing nutcracker woman in her scarlet surgeon's outfit before me once more, and it was easy for me to make the decision. Either you submitted to the blows of Fate, or if you wanted to arm yourself against them you must sacrifice certain things, even yourself, on the altar of comfort. 'There is only *one* innate error: to believe that we are here to be happy.' Who said that, you ask? Well, who do you think?

One last, yearning look back at the flat where they'd have to dispense with my purr in future, one last farewell meditation on my beloved stainless steel bowls, bowls which had sometimes seemed to me as full of promise as the teats of the mother I never knew, and one final farewell in the spirit to that total nincompoop Gustav (Gustav before his brainwashing, that is), and then I was off. I wiped the tears from the fur of my face with my right forepaw, choked back a sob, and took the first step into freedom.[4]

My journey to the heart of darkness began with an ordinary jump. I dropped from the window to the balcony and from the balcony to the terrace below. Using tortuous race-tracks above the walls and secret gaps in garden fences known to no one but me, I soon reached the well-tended jungle of rhododendrons and ornamental shrubs. From here I could have found the way out to the street through a gap between the buildings in my sleep. A short sprint along the pavement parallel to the way I'd already taken through the gardens, and within seconds I was back outside the building I'd just left. Humans are dependent on doors, steps and direct paths, since their bone structure and musculature, retarded in a pitiful state of inflexibility, seem to leave them no option but to move along regular tracks like an antediluvian locomotive groaning under its own weight. The whole business becomes particularly painful when they employ the very latest metering devices to make meticulous records of their lack of athletic prowess at the various Olympic Games meetings they hold. They even show it all live on television and end up awarding themselves cups and medals for the miserable results. Come to think of it, we're inferior to them only in respect of stamina. I expect they need all that stamina to bear the thought of their physical uselessness.

By now the rain, which was coming down harder all the time, had made me very wet. When I looked up at the ground-floor flat in the old building, I realised to my surprise that it already seemed strange to me. For as the mighty building rose to the angry sky in the darkness, the paint on its façade peeling like the skin of a putrefying corpse to reveal stained grey stone, the windows like eye sockets in an emaciated head, I felt no sense of familiarity any more. It was as if I'd never lived in that building, never had a friend there, never shared his joys and sorrows. Suddenly it was just an old dump like any other crying out for luxury renovation. Good: that meant I needn't shed a tear for the amazing bulbous oriels and the basalt heads of demons set under the cornice, guaranteed to keep evil spirits away. I'd obviously had enough of the place and my boringly conventional life there anyway.

I trotted on along the pavement, following my nose, while the spring shower gave me a foretaste of something more like a summer splash. Incidentally, it's not true that we hate water. We just don't like being bathed, because unlike human beings we are always clean. Of course I knew my way about the immediate vicinity; I'd often been out and about in this district. Tonight, however, the place didn't seem at all familiar, but on the contrary downright foreign and threatening. The picturesque old street lights were like absurdly tall, lanky spies with opaque faces. The asphalt, which had a film of water rippling over it, was a ramp leading to the unknown, giving the impression it might come to a sudden end any moment and cast me into the deepest chasms of horror. Since I really knew these parts like the back of my paw, why did they suddenly seem so sombre? Surely it wasn't because I knew there was no going back now to the fluffy sheepskin rug in front of the crackling fire? That's unworthy of you, I told myself angrily, you haven't gone a hundred metres from hell yet, and you already feel tempted by all that bourgeois soft soap! Concentrate on your nuts, you effeminate fool, think of those nuts which will rise in summer like twin suns in a blazing firmament!

Spurred on by such thoughts, I marched automatically on as the storm gradually became a raging tempest. I was wondering if I'd win the Nobel Prize for proposing, as a new natural law, the simple fact that you're spoilt rotten for all the comforts of life so long as you don't lack for anything in any case, whereas no end of horrible things happen, instantly and all at once, just when you're in need. Why else must I find myself on the set of a bad film about the cruel sea just now, at the beginning of my glorious flight? To all appearances I was reduced to half my normal size, since my coat was drenched with rainwater, its wet fur clinging to my body like a marten's. Anyone who'd seen me in this state probably couldn't even have said what species I belonged to. Complicated flashes of forked lightning tore through the sky, showing the full extent of the flood in their sudden spotlights. The rain was now falling like great sweeping veils of water. The water-level in the street was rising perceptibly, and soon reached the dimensions of a small river. Everywhere, unfastened window-shutters slammed deafeningly against walls, branches were torn off trees and fell in the road, dustbins were overturned by powerful gusts of wind, and the penetrating rattle of raindrops on car roofs provided just the right rhythmic bass accompaniment to these outstanding soloists.

I stopped and thought. Couldn't I pick some better moment to set off on my travels? It might be sensible to shelter in the doorway of a building before I started to resemble those contemporaries of mine who like sleeping in washing-machine drums, and wake up – if they wake up at all – to find themselves in a fascinating underwater world full of sock eels and knicker jellyfish. In fact it would be an even better idea to sprint home to Gustav's, take a rest there to dry off, and try another jail-break when the storm had died down and my strength was restored. Although it meant going against all my good resolutions, I decided on the latter course of action. Easier said than done, though: when I tried putting my plan of retreat into practice I had a new problem to cope with – by this time I was hopelessly lost. The street where I found myself was very much the same as all the others in this old part of town. Furthermore, the curtain of rain meant that I seemed to be looking at every building, every front garden with curly cast-iron railings and every antiquated alley through a pair of steamed-up diving goggles. I should have paid more attention to the signs bearing street names during my previous clandestine excursions. Unfortunately, from unthinking habit I'd always preferred the specific technique of my own kind and made a scent-map of the town in my head from the marks my colleagues left behind them. And not surprisingly, this special kind of cartography failed me in a thorough heavy-wash programme like the present one. Of course I still had vague recollections of the occasional unusual building, and I could visualise a few major road junctions, but now even these few rudimentary means of orientation merged into a tangle of street-scapes in general.

Within a few minutes the euphoria of my departure had turned to sheer panic. The raging storm had washed away not only the dirt in the streets but all my daydreams about a Francis living wild, welcomed into the freedom of nature as if into his mother's bosom. My dearest wish was to get home as fast as possible, snuggle up to the radiator and stay there until I could be served for dinner as a nice roast. Let's face it, didn't sex usually prove a damn nerve-racking, exhausting business, and wasn't the pleasure achieved seldom worth the effort? Surely the world was over-populated enough. Shouldn't sexual intercourse be a pleasure best left to my more ordinary contemporaries, people too stupid and lazy to read a good book, people who took a compulsive interest in their genitals and the brainless amusement they provided instead? Yes, it should. I'd wave goodbye to my nuts and read good books for the rest of my days. And now to get out of here!

A flash, a crack of thunder, and in the glaring light a caprice of the stormy wind showed me a curtain of rain parting in the middle to reveal the mouth of a dark alley paved with cobblestones. I thought I'd come down that alley. It led to a road junction; so did the street where I now stood, which had quite a steep slope to it. I gazed at the alley, transfixed, until the bright lightning disappeared. Maybe it was my imagination, but I thought I really did recognise a familiar spot. Since the alley was on the other side of the street, seen from my present standpoint, my best course of action would be to cross the road diagonally and then turn right at the junction. It would mean wading paw-deep in the water flowing down the street like a shallow stream, but it would be worth the effort in the end.

I stepped into the water rippling by and hurried to the middle of the road. As a result I finally enjoyed total immersion, but in my present condition that didn't matter. The closer I came to my goal, the more clearly did the dim light of the street lamp on the corner show me the manhole cover in the middle of the road junction quivering as if shaken by a phantom hand. The gratings in the gutters on both sides of the street were swallowing a good deal of the flood, but things must be chaotic down in the sewers in such torrential rain, leading to the risk of sudden eruptions of sewage here and there. The immense pressure might force manhole covers off. So it would be sensible to get a move on and reach the alley before I was faced with any such unpleasant situation. Just as this thought shot through my head, I heard a rushing and roaring behind me as if the Atlantic Ocean in person was coming to town. I whisked round and looked for whatever was making the noise. Aghast, I watched as a tidal wave about half a metre high and stretching right across the street came foaming and raging round the corner and rolled on towards me at high speed. Bloody hell, had all the natural disasters in the universe just been waiting for me to take my first step into independence? No, not all of them – there were still some to come. For when I turned my head forward again to check out the best way of escape, I was horrified to see the manhole cover in the middle of the road junction tossed in the air by a mighty jet of water from underground. The paralysis induced in me by these moments of terror was my undoing. I'd lingered too long staring at the spectacle, and before I knew it, before I could get away from the middle of the road, the wave caught me from behind and flung me to the ground. I struggled to get some kind of footing, but the fury of the wild water forced my body to curl up into a ball and drove me on full speed ahead, like a car tyre come loose. The comparison with those of my kind who like sleeping in washing-machine drums was extremely apt now, for in this unfortunate situation all I could do was swallow water, strike out helplessly with all four paws and hope the wave would soon roll on and over me, leaving its victim behind like driftwood.

Although I couldn't concentrate on anything but sheer survival as I performed death-defying acrobatics in the belly of the wave, I saw out of the corner of my eye that I had now been washed dangerously close to the open sewer shaft. The latter had a particularly intriguing surprise ready to spring on me. For whereas the sludgy brown contents of its stomach had spewed up at the road junction like a liquid mushroom cloud, it was now acting like a whirlpool in a stormy sea, sucking all the water round it back down again with a crazy thirst. You couldn't call me a particularly timid type, but my bladder spontaneously emptied at the sight, enriching the waters foaming around me, for the simple reason that never in my wildest dreams had I envisaged myself drowning in the smelly vortex of the sewage system. I always expected to pop my clogs in old age, sitting on a velvet cushion, either from choking on a fist-sized chunk of liver or from fracturing my Adam's apple with shrill cries of lust while having it off with the Siamese queen next door. All this in radiant sunshine and to the accompaniment of Mahler's *Kindertotenlieder*, of course. But why so defeatist? It didn't have to turn out that way. The tidal wave wasn't necessarily going to wash me down that tiny hole – after all, it was a big road junction. No, not necessarily . . .

After what seemed to me my three hundred and eleventh somersault, I saw the full glory of the open manhole right in front of me like some creepy prophecy come true. The tremendous suction from inside created a spiralling vortex at the top, circling slowly, but inexorably drawing in all the water and rubbish near by. It looked like the glowing eye of the Cyclops himself. I'd have liked to put up a final prayer to my Creator, who for some strange reason had obviously decided I was to go to a better world by way of an intake of human excretions. But before I could get that far, the wave brought me to the edge of the whirlpool. The whirlpool promptly demonstrated its power and sucked me into its orbit with all its might. I screeched, lashed out with my paws and tried a couple of feeble swimming strokes to escape its hellish powers of suction. I was wasting my time. Like an ant, I was washed round and round in the eddying water at the top of the manhole several times, and then I was finally dragged down into the depths.

In retrospect I see my involuntary venture into aquatics as if through a dirty, scratched plastic film. I remember feeling an urgent need for oxygen and opening my mouth as soon as I was in the water and going down. That was about the silliest thing I could have done, for what little air remained in my lungs was instantly replaced by water. Even worse than the physical shock was the feeling that in my helpless desperation I was on the point of drifting off into mental derangement. Moreover my body, like a living torpedo, kept knocking against the iron rungs cemented into the cylindrical interior of the shaft. But though I was nearly unconscious by now, and it was pitch dark inside the shaft, my highly receptive sense of sight showed me first a series of air bubbles splashing past, then the glimmer of something like a metal bar passing along the winding sewers below. Then I stopped falling, and just as I identified the bar as a hand-rail I collided with it, belly first. I stayed hanging there like a fox's brush soaked in water. The sudden impact, in its turn, brought all the liquid I'd swallowed spewing out of my insides as if it were rendering first aid. Obviously the whirlpool I'd been dragged into was the final consignment from above, because all I could feel now was a last trickle flowing down my back and then sloshing around on the stone floor.

Too badly battered by Fate to make any movement of its own, my body swung rhythmically to and fro where it lay draped over the hand-rail, until it finally dropped backwards to the floor. Once down, it curled up snake-like into a kind of spiral, and the water still in my lungs trickled out of the corners of my mouth. Although I'm equipped with the best optical system in the world, one which leaves even the residual-light cameras people use for nocturnal photography literally in the shade, I couldn't make out anything in my new surroundings at first, just overwhelming blackness. The rain went on splashing down on my fur through the open manhole, but judging by the small number of drops that hit their target I concluded that it must have slackened off. Typically, once the damage was done the perpetrator made a quick get-away. My battered body was sending me the most alarming signals of pain from every nerve ending, but I couldn't be sure whether or not I'd broken anything as I fell. However, I dared not move; I was too scared I'd find I was paralysed. And if so, what dreadful death confronted me? Unable to move from the spot, I'd be torn to pieces slowly and with relish by mice, or more likely rats who could match me for physical size. There were sure to be plenty of rats going about their nasty business down in this clammy vault. And all the time I'd be fully conscious, aware of every detail of my mutilations, watching it all *with the best optical system in the world*!

Following a time-honoured custom of the days when I woke happy, I did finally summon up the courage to shoot a claw out of the fold of skin covering the pad of my right forepaw. Gradually all the rest of my claws came out like miniature flick-knives. My wet body was overcome by a violent fit of shaking which sprayed water everywhere, and before any further tricks to get me up to starting temperature could ensue I pulled myself together and jumped up. Pains shot through my guts like demons unleashed. I held my breath, because the torment threatened to overcome me in short order. The injuries every fibre of my body had suffered throbbed and hammered so horribly that I yelled out loud. But I'd been fortunate in my misfortune. So far as I could tell from a few experimental stretches – which were painful but bearable – I didn't seem to have broken anything, and the bruises from all that bumping about weren't really too bad either. In short, I rearranged my bones and sinews and offered thanks to the Great Reaper, who seemed to have turned a blind eye my way again.

The thing now was to get away from this filthy place of perdition as quickly as possible. Slowly, and somewhat handicapped by a numbing crick in my neck, I raised my head and looked up at the infernal chasm above, my way down to the underworld. The open manhole showed the heavens with ominous, towering clouds still driving across them. But occasionally patches of blue morning sky broke the darkness, allowing dim light to fall into the shaft. However, this faint light didn't seem to promise a happy ending, more like the exact opposite. Because now I could see that the iron rungs were too far apart for me to use them to work my way up. Even if I stood on my back legs on one rung, which I couldn't anyway, for reasons of balance, my body wouldn't stretch far enough to reach the next rung above. It looked as if I had no choice but to wander around this crypt until I found some other way out. Perhaps I'd thanked the Great Reaper too soon: OK, so the fall hadn't killed me, but it was to be feared that the smell of sewage, which was getting more and more penetrating as my pain subsided, would make a thorough job of it before too long.

I turned round, and had another surprise. By now my eyes had accustomed themselves to the poor light, and I could take in every aspect of the dubious charms of my present location. It looked as if I was on the bank of a canal about three metres broad, of unknown length, a picturesque river of piss and shit bounded by an ancient, curving wall which threw back the quirky reflections of the sludge as it quietly flowed past. It was difficult to make out where this sewer began and where it ended, for the cold light falling through the shaft cast a dull glow only over my immediate surroundings. The quay on which I stood, with its rusty hand-rail, was in fact a niche; the sewage workers would climb down to this point before setting off through the tunnels. There was a walkway about a metre wide, also made of stone, on both sides of the sewer. I had no idea where this path would lead me, but it would be rotten luck if I didn't come upon a link with the world of daylight somewhere along the way. After such a concentrated set of misfortunes, the law of averages said something nice must happen to me soon.

Although the nauseating smell and the musty, claustrophobic atmosphere of my cramped quarters didn't exactly suggest Venice, this gloomy spot had a certain morbidly romantic charm of its own. Before I'd honoured the bowels of the city with my radiant presence, the stormy floods must have caused one hell of a blockage there. Now that the tide had gone down, water-drops were falling from the roof of the tunnel into the sewer as if they were dripping from stalactites in a cave, echoing again and again, making some very odd noises. The pattern of the ripples reflected on the walls was the visual counterpart of the weird acoustics, and the constant quiet murmur of the main stream provided comforting background music, putting the finishing touch to the not unattractive picture of a grisly grotto. Partly to relish my relief at finding I was still all in one piece, partly because

I suddenly felt fascinated by this kingdom of shadows, I stood on the edge of the stone path, legs planted wide apart, and took in the weird scene. Somehow the hypnotic lullaby of the never-ending, echoing drip-drip-drip and the peculiar atmosphere of this unlikely place soothed me, making me feel strangely peaceful. How idyllically this little river flowed along, what meditations it induced as one stood on the bank, letting one's eyes stray over the gentle waves. Look, there was even a swan swimming in the distance . . .

Swan? Come off it, you didn't get swans in the sewage system. Crocodiles, maybe, but no swans. There really *was* something swimming in the sewer, though, something white drifting towards me, a bloated something that turned majestically round and round on its own axis. It emerged from the darkness as unexpectedly as a shining space ship emerging from the belly of the universe. At first it was only a tiny white dot, bobbing about in the pitch-black expanses of the water. It was only its whiteness that made me notice it. But the closer it came the more clearly I could make it out. Now that it was about twenty metres away it looked like a fluffy, puffed-up flour bag. My harmonious feelings of a moment ago began giving way to a vague sense of oppression that constricted my throat like an iron collar. I couldn't take my eyes off this uncanny buoy, especially as it was bobbing along straight towards me. After a while I could see that the apparition wasn't as bright a white as it had initially seemed: it was the corpse of an animal with milk-white fur which was now very dirty, and it had been in the water so long that it had swelled to twice its natural size and looked like a sodden cotton wool ball. So I was looking at a drowned body. And the nightmare showed it could get even worse. There were large wounds in the lifeless corpse, going deep into the victim's flesh and suggesting small bomb craters. There were too many of them to be counted; they had probably been caused by bites. Since the corpse was in an advanced state of decomposition, and there was no blood flowing from the wounds, which ranged from dark pink to violet in colour, I guessed that death must have occurred several days ago. Ergo, the deceased had begun his wanderings from some very distant part of the sewage system, probably right outside town, and had been floating endlessly in the labyrinth of the sewers ever since.

I'd been fearing another revelation for quite some time, and now it came. Moving elegantly, like an aquatic ballerina, a tail chopped off in the middle suddenly rose from the poor tortured body, and I recognised it as a member of my own species floating there like a grotesque lifebelt. Horror and panic exploded in me, as if defective blood vessels were bursting in my brain. Creepy speculation about what kind of maltreatment had changed one of my own kind from a clean-limbed athlete to a badly mutilated lump of flesh occupied my entire mind, and I forgot all about my own aches and pains. I expected to glean further information very soon, in particular on the corpse's breed, because it was making straight for the side of the stone walkway, so I'd be able to see its face as the body gently rotated.

However, the face turned out to be the most horrible sight of all. The corpse did indeed come closer, almost brushing against the walkway; it came so close I could practically touch it. And yes, it turned gracefully on its own axis like a drifting water-lily and showed its front view. Enough light fell on it to let me see everything clearly. But horror of horrors, there was nothing left to see! The body, resembling a cake which had risen beyond all expectations, had no head left at all. That valuable item had simply been torn off, and nothing now hung from the neck but blackened fringes of flesh like the leaves of plants dipping picturesquely into the water. The corpse went on turning, and I could see the full extent of what had been done to it. The battle must have been an unequal one from the start, something like the battle of

David and Goliath but without the biblical result. Obviously the stronger contestant had never entertained any idea of doing his opponent a favour and carrying out the execution with a single merciful bite, in our old hunting tradition. The slaughter had been done with such hatred, or rather such perverse pleasure in inflicting pain, that the victor had bitten whole chunks out of the victim just for fun. Poor thing, he must have been suffering such pain and desperation that he didn't know how to defend himself. So then the monster went for the throat, digging his teeth right in and tearing so furiously that the head was finally severed from the backbone, hanging loose, attached to the body only like a lid on a rusty hinge. After that, for some mysterious reason or other, the murderer removed it altogether and somehow managed to tip the lifeless body into the sewers.

The unimaginable brutality of it literally took my breath away. Ugh! It was a horrible picture, much worse than all the visions of amputation I'd seen in my imagination when Francesca started in on her nuts project. As the headless body circled and floated past me, disappearing into the darkness again, I wondered who could have done such a thing to a defenceless creature – and most of all, why. Although the victim had lost his head, which made it harder for me to identify the breed, the body, even deformed as it was, told my expert eye that this had been an ordinary European Shorthair. The members of this breed weren't exactly famous for wholesale aggression, and they certainly didn't go gunning for jokers whose fangs were drooling with murderous lust. But was the monstrous murderer necessarily an animal? *Homo sapiens* was more given to such bloodthirsty goings-on, to the infliction of pointless violence just for the fun to be got out of suffering. There was one good argument against this theory, however: humans like to use instruments of various kinds when practising torture. Those instruments are symbols of their power – are even glorified in their culture as fetishes. As far as I could tell, however, the injuries inflicted in this case had not been made by knives, scalpels or sharp, pointed objects. No, they were the work of elemental, unadulterated violence arising from a natural and insatiable lust for blood. I hated to admit it to myself, but the whole thing looked horribly like one of those inexplicable fits of brutality in which my own kind sometimes indulge.

The horrific object was drifting away again. In my imagination it turned into a floating coffin decked with flowers, the sort of funeral people still give the dead today in some exotic cultures. Finally the darkness swallowed it up. I looked the way it had gone for some time longer, as if hypnotised, full of deep and genuine grief. As I stood there I imagined how this fellow member of my species might have looked in life. His fur, white as blossom, must surely have shone in the midday sun like dazzling snow; his sapphire eyes would have seemed to bore right through a chance observer if their glances met. And when he slept by a glowing fire on a frosty winter evening, stretching and flexing his muscles as if in a trance, he must have been over a metre long. He had certainly been a rare jewel of his species, in fact the cat's whiskers, and a source of fascination to one and all. So it was particularly shattering to think of his meeting such a dreadful, undignified end. 'Goodbye, white stranger,' I said at last, out loud. 'We shall meet in heaven.'

Good grief, what did I think I was up to? Hadn't I anything better to do than mourn an unknown corpse and deliver melancholy funeral orations? How did I know the gourmet who had learnt to know and love the deceased as cocktail nibbles wasn't lying in wait right now, somewhere near at hand, following the course of my investigations with a grin and indulging in culinary fantasies as his belly rumbled? I was in a kind of anteroom to hell, after all, a place into which those above off-loaded all their nastier and less attractive products, consigning them to the process of decay. There were no Gustavs here to step in at the last moment if some deranged cannibal went for my windpipe, no offices with nostalgic old telephones where the Philip Marlowe of the pointy-eared race could retreat when his detective work was done. There was nothing here but gloom, damp and dirt – and eerily bloated corpses. And who knew, perhaps there really were dear little goblins living in the sewers who usually ate shit and drank industrial waste, but might fancy a change from their usual diet if a small creature on his travels fetched up in their domain? I imagined them as slavering horror versions of some supermarket chain's consumer research project . . .

As if my negative thinking had actually conjured up the evil thing itself, I suddenly heard a stealthy rustling. It resonated through the tunnel and then mingled with the echoes of the drops and those other eerie noises which probably came from the imperceptible 'breathing' of such a huge stone maze. Before I could erect my fur into bristles with alarm and arch my back in defence, I heard another rustling sound, rather closer this time. I tried and failed to decide which direction it was coming from. In rapid succession, like a motor-driven camera rattling away, my eyes fixed on all the unlit corners from which a monster might spring at any moment, on all the dancing shadows on the walls. Discouraged, I realised there was nothing to be seen. Yet I instinctively felt that these transient noises couldn't be put down either to my overheated imagination or to any chance activity that happened to produce sound. At a moment of suspense like this in a thriller movie you generally see the hero's black colleague emerge from the darkness, whereupon the hero breathes a sigh of relief because that explains the creaking door which made his flesh creep. I wasn't sure if I'd have found a variant on that theme particularly reassuring just now. Calling on my common sense, therefore, I decided to put my previous plan into action: I'd go on along the walkway until I found some way out of the sewers, and never mind how often the ghosts rattled their chains to scare me.

With studied indifference, as if I'd seen enough of some breathtaking natural scene, I turned away from the waters of the sewer and marched straight into the dark. It was like plunging into some amorphous living mass with the terrible certainty of never getting out again. Now and then I took a surreptitious backward glance, looking about as inconspicuous as a shoplifter hiding a fridge under his T-shirt. As I did so I thought I saw shadows of an even more dubious nature flitting around the bottom of the sewer shaft, which was filled with blue light and growing smaller and smaller behind me. Was the paranoia that had surely been caused by the claustrophobic conditions of these catacombs already turning to outright hallucinations? I'd happily have invested total conviction in this theory, putting my persecution mania and the way my teeth chattered with fear down to the shock of finding the corpse, if only . . . if only I hadn't heard that nerve-racking rustling again. But it wasn't a rustling this time. It was a shuffling and a secret scuffling, a growling and a scratching. And suddenly it wasn't just coming from behind me but from everywhere, every nook and cranny. As I quickened my pace and finally broke into a frantic gallop, I risked another glance behind me. This time I couldn't pretend I was suffering from optical illusions and nervous tension induced by fear. For now I saw distinct moving silhouettes outlined before the lighter background. What made my heart hammer to the rhythm of a heavy metal beat was the fact that *they*, whoever they might be, were emerging from their hidey-holes in such numbers, as if a signal had been given. All of a sudden there was a gigantic army of shadows close on my heels. And though I couldn't see anything ahead of me in the dark I could feel, with physical certainty, that an equally large troop was approaching from that direction. Good God, where had these bastards sprung from all of a sudden, and what were they?

Rats! Of course, a sewer without rats would be like a cemetery without well-fed worms, the kind of worms who on reaching pensionable age have the nerve to demand high premiums from their successors for their own particular sections of a grave. With the delightful little difference that rats of this sort obviously ate my kind. For safety's sake I kept up my high speed, hoping the way out of this horrible nightmare which I longed for might appear before me any moment, like an oasis appearing to someone dying of thirst in the desert. But the mob on my heels seemed to be highly motivated too and was rapidly closing in. A last glance back made me shudder. Like a severely overweight black snake, an apparently endless legion of indefinable creatures was moving along behind me, and the word 'legion' really hit the nail on the head, since this pack was obviously running in orderly ranks; there would be no headlong rush with individual members of the pack getting in each other's way. It was an army marching on soft paws, a purposeful army, driving me into a corner and already sure of victory. No doubt its strategy of quiet attack had proved successful more than once before. The light behind these soldiers shone on their backs and showed the outlines of hairs, from which I concluded that like me they had fur. Unusually for mammals of my category, however, their eyes did not shine in the dark. In my kind, that effect is caused by the reflective layer in our eyes, a mirror-like structure extending behind most of the retina. It is present in most other nocturnal animals as well, and reflects light which is not absorbed by the retina when it first enters the eye. This gives the retina an additional luminous stimulus, increasing the sensitivity of vision in poor light. Of course there was very little brightness here anyway, so the eye-shine effect wouldn't necessarily have been on view, but I'd have bet my own peepers were shining like the

Stop signals at a level crossing right now. There seemed to be something in my theory of a bestially mutated consumer group after all.

Then the miracle happened! About twenty metres ahead I actually saw a ray of light emerging from the bottom of the wall on my right and shining diagonally down into the sewer like a dazzling lance. It probably came from the inlet of a drainpipe slanting down from the street to carry off rainwater. Since day must have dawned some time ago, light could now come into the sewers through the drainpipe. With a bit of luck I might be able to wriggle up it to the world above and escape my pursuers. In sudden euphoria I switched to turbo drive, like an athlete putting on a final spurt at the end of the thousand metres, and raced on as fast as my tired joints would go. The lance of light, which was getting brighter every moment and seemed to cut the gloomy sewer in two, was approaching at amazing speed, and I was delighted to find that the sound of the mob after me soon died away. Another ten metres, another five metres, another two metres; that shining hole in the wall looked more and more like a magic gate beyond which outright madness would drop away, and such unjustly criticised phenomena as addiction to TV, the weekend glooms, Monday-morning feelings, in fact the normality of ordinary life would begin again. At last I reached the longed-for passage to freedom and prepared for a sharp right turn. The monsters could seethe in bitter frustration or eat each other up for all I cared . . .

The colossus emerged from the bright hole in the wall as suddenly as a super-tanker from a bank of fog just before a collision. As I tried to slam the emergency brakes on I thought I'd run straight into some goddam dog – a dog which had gone to the bad and turned into a monster, though. About a metre before this imposing figure I stumbled, lost my balance, fell over, turned a full somersault and finally landed in front of its shaggy paws. Expecting it to be already bending down to smash my head in, I opened my eyes a crack, out of sheer masochism, and looked straight at its face. It looked even freakier and more dangerous from ground level than stomach level, a phrase to be taken literally, because even on my feet I only came up to its belly. Despite its monstrous size I immediately saw that it wasn't a dog at all, but one of my own species, a Chartreux.[5] This fellow had his breed's typical and enviably dense short, smoky blue coat, although it was so full of sewage sludge that the soft and downy texture of the fur was largely lost. His type also showed in the healthily compact build often regarded by the ignorant as obesity, although in this particular specimen the muscle and extra fat tissue had combined so happily that it was hard to be sure if you were facing a tub of lard or a muscle man boasting resilience and elasticity. In any case he was incredibly large, in fact massive, and above all he was absolutely terrifying. He did, however, differ from the usual variety of neighbourhood tyrant in three respects, and they froze the blood in my veins. The first difference seemed pretty harmless compared to the other two: this giant stank so much you'd have thought he went diving for treasure in the sewers every day of his life. I didn't know whether to throw up straight away or wait until he'd exercised his own operating technique on my oesophagus. The second difference was more alarming. He had no eyes. I mean, he had eyeballs all right, but they were covered with a milky film, like a lighter version of cataract. Set in his blue-grey face, these milky orbs had a particularly grotesque effect, giving their owner the scary look of a sinister medieval dabbler in the black arts. My intending murderer was blind as a bat. Unlike human beings, however, he didn't necessarily need eyes to get his bearings – and certainly not to kill! Third and last, there were his earrings; golden earrings, strangely clean for all his dirt and shining in the eerie light. His earlobes were very ragged; the earrings probably got caught in various objects from time to time and had made more space for themselves.

The executioner of my fate stood there in the flood of light, a mighty, indeed almighty figure, and as improbable a sight as a Christmas goose found horrifically resurrected when you open the fridge door. He stared intently down at me with his white eyes, as if wondering which of my organs would taste best. His pale coat, patterned with encrusted dirt and bare patches left by rat-bites, gave his huge body the look of a threadbare Bruin costume as worn by 'resting' actors performing at children's birthday parties. After a while he raised his head with extraordinary grace and looked around him. I imitated him, following the direction of his blind gaze. What I then saw made my bladder want to empty itself again with the shock, but unfortunately it was empty already. The army which had been chasing me had caught up and formed a dense crowd around me. Each member of the audience seemed to be a faithful copy of the big boss. Only a few of them were of the Chartreux breed, of course, so far as you could tell one breed from another at all in this dim light, and none of them wore gold earrings, so I concluded that my opponent must be someone quite out of the ordinary. But they all stank to high heaven, they all had scarred coats matted with sewage sludge, and all of them, absolutely all of them, were blind, staring at me with those milky, useless eyes.

There was a disturbance of some kind behind the front row of the circle. Apparently the dinner gong had sounded and the troops at the back wanted to get their noses in the trough. The awesome old character with the matted whiskers bent down to me, a sardonic smile crossing his broad and dirty face.

'Your hour has come, little one!' he said in a deep bass voice reminiscent of the growling of villainous actors in movies about the drugs Mafia.

Instead of trying a retort – such as: 'Listen, I can tell you where to buy really fabulous tinned food' – I asked myself for the nth time why I'd ever been fool enough to run away. By now I could have come round from the anaesthetic, admired my new streamlined anatomy in the mirror, eaten a hearty meal and entered upon a new life free of all the fuss and bother of sex. I could have survived, dammit! And above all I could have followed the advice of the ever-reliable Schopenhauer, who unerringly spotted the dangers of making vital decisions without sufficient thought, over a century ago, and warned idiots like me that: 'We may not have to atone for evil-doing until the next world, but we pay for stupidity in this one . . . '

CHAPTER 3

'... although justice may occasionally be tempered with mercy.' I finish the quotation just to make things tidy, but expecting mercy from a horde of cannibals was rather like requesting estate agents to turn over three-quarters of their profits to a charitable housing project. These blind restaurant critics – probably from the *Good Carrion Guide* – were staring at me in a manner which suggested it would be a merciful act if they tore my head off first and started tucking into Fillet Steaks Francis later.

A gazelle-like creature came into view behind Big Daddy Golden Earring. Obviously she couldn't wait for the gruesome buffet to open. Swift as an arrow, however, the boss's great club of a paw shot up. It struck the eager lady's chest with a hollow thud, stopping her in her tracks. She was a sinewy young thing, still growing, and her matt coat was even blacker than this black inferno itself could ever be. Her ears, once so sensitive, had lost their original funnel shape and were now ragged and shredded, either by countless battles with other warriors or the furious resistance put up by rats at bay. A scarf which had been lying in a drawer for years providing a home for moths couldn't have looked worse. There was an ugly scar across her face, perhaps a memento left by some startled sewage worker's sharp metal tool. Her muscular figure resembled that of a pure-bred greyhound; she must be an Oriental. She might have a punk look, but her eyes, icily iridescent as neon, and the claws protruding like murderous sickles from her paw pads, told me I'd come out of a duel with this wiry lady as mincemeat. This, in short, was a young witch who liked to cook herself up some blood broth on occasion.

'Come on, little one, aren't you going to make a break for it?' asked the Prince of Darkness with mock concern. Misty vapour seemed to swirl in his eyes.

Well, guess what! He had a sense of humour. Not being the melancholy sort myself, I replied, 'Certainly not, old chap! It's quite a treat to meet comrades in a lonely spot like this. Inspires one with confidence.'

'You'd have a fair chance, though. After all, our eyes aren't in working order, and we'll give you a start to add to the fun.'

'Ah, but you see I've always wanted to meet you lot. When I heard you were so clean you actually lived down the loo I abandoned my bungee-jump training right away and came straight here.'

The virago got sick of hearing me answer back. Angrily, she laid her ears back, showing the perfect wedge of her head, and opened her eyes wide. Then she raced out in front of the assembled team, claws like scalpels reaching longingly for yours truly.

'That's enough silly jokes! We must eliminate him or he'll give us away, like all the others.'

I had the suicidal nerve to suggest, 'If that's all that's worrying you, ma'am, surely amputation of the tongue would do the trick?'

Suddenly the boss lost his sense of humour. His milky eyeballs seemed clouded, as if with some dark liquid, and the mockery in his bulldog face suddenly and alarmingly changed to deadly earnest. At this the monstrous rabble fell perfectly silent and waited, motionless, as if to make sure the emperor of the sewers wasn't distracted from passing sentence by such irritating sounds as the rumbling of stomachs. In fact even though I was in such desperate danger, I couldn't help rather liking them. The light from the drainpipe gave their matted coats a silvery shimmer, making them resemble fans of a heavy metal band famed for its excesses on stage. Their pale eyes, hundreds of pairs of pale eyes standing out in the dark, might have been sparklers lit during the performance of a favourite song, and their bitten ears symbolic of the injuries you risk by indulging in too much consumption of such loud music. At bottom these children of eternal night were an extreme example of our own nature, representing us all as we wander silently in the dark realms of our souls.

Of course it might have been an idea to give a thought to my chances of flight in this nasty situation. But yet again my active brain and my incorrigible curiosity got the better of me. They made me stop and ask myself a few questions. For instance, what strange circumstances had brought all these animals down to the underworld? And why were they afflicted with blindness? Or had they always been blind? Why did they kill others of their kind? Because the sewage system was short of prey? In that case why didn't they finish eating their dead colleagues' bodies? And finally, the sixty-thousand dollar question: if they spent their whole time down here and never saw the light of day, why didn't they suffer from rickets?[6]

Thank God, however, it looked as if I'd soon be cured of my compulsive curiosity for good. The old boss remained lost in thought for a while, making the few uncouth facial expressions of which he was capable, and then shook himself hard (sending a number of clumps of caked mud flying) and solemnly pronounced judgement.

'You're right, brothers and sisters,' he said, indicating the Amazon who was still glaring accusingly in my direction. 'He must be eliminated. The number of fools visiting the

Catacombs of Mercy is increasing daily. They come for cheap thrills and cunningly turn our weakness to their own ends. We've degenerated into attractions in some goddam sideshow of freaks. And they don't stop at spying on us either. Once they get back up above again they show off – they pretend their timid explorations were daring adventures, thus encouraging others to follow their example. And this reprehensible behaviour only serves to attract human attention to us. One of these days humans will learn our secret too, and then they'll send a disinfection squad down into the sewers to finish us off. We know we're doomed to die, dear brothers and sisters, and we don't fear death. But our mission, our sacred mission – who will carry it out then? Who will save all the lost souls, the souls who have died to rise again? Who will save the children, brothers and sisters?'

'Save the children! Save the children! Save the children!" the whole pack of them cried, speaking as one. I raised myself from my supine position, sat up on my hind legs and observed the effects of the high priest's clever oratory in amazement. As the blind often will in excitement, this grubby lot were weaving their heads back and forth in a regular pattern of movement. While they did so they kept on urging each other to save these apparently significant children, who were obviously dear to their hearts. Their chant was accompanied by spasmodic twitchings. I was just forming a hypothesis about the subject of their lament when, all of a sudden, I actually saw them – the children, I mean. They were clinging like young penguins between the front legs of the older females, snuggling close to the shaggy belly fur and half covered by the chest fur. That was why I hadn't noticed them before. They still had a little colour left in the irises of their eyes, so I concluded that they hadn't gone completely blind yet. By comparison with the adults, their fur was sparkling clean, suggesting that much loving care had been lavished on it. But there was something else which really surprised me. In every case, the adult females and the children they were caring for were of different breeds. A baby Siamese, for instance, was sheltering under the wing of a sturdy Maine Coon, and a young Birman female was being mothered by an Egyptian Mau with only one incisor left. Even allowing for the chance effects of interbreeding, the obvious difference between mothers and children was so striking that I had to assume these were all cases of adoption.

'We know the tale of our sad past, brothers and sisters, we know our fate,' said the big boss, picking up the thread of his discourse again and symbolically waving the uproar down to a tolerable level with his paws. The matronly wet-nurses were scowling at me as if I'd contradicted his last remarks.

'And since we know our fate so well, we are in duty bound to it. But how can we do our job properly when idiots keep putting irresponsible members of our own species on our tracks, and there's a danger they may set humans after us too? It's high time to make an example of someone.'

'Suppose I were to tell you I suffer from severe amnesia?' I desperately suggested, trying for a stay of execution. 'For instance, blow me if I haven't gone and forgotten my name again! Now was it Mimi or was it Pussy? Hold on, I believe it was Pinky . . . '

What, no applause? No roars of laughter such as you get in a TV sitcom when the soundtrack fires off a gag? I was obviously the only member of my own audience able to see anything amusing in my clowning. Well, I could understand that it wouldn't seem so funny if you were already visualising the comic as lunch, chopped into fraternal portions, share and share alike. The Chartreux turned his blind gaze on me again. It was like encountering the rotating floodlight beam of some gruesome lighthouse.

'I'm sorry, little one,' he said, sounding like a father ruefully holding an empty bag of sweets in front of his little boy's nose. 'Nothing personal, you understand. We have to draw the line somewhere, to protect ourselves and our work, and you just happened to be in the wrong place at the wrong time.'

'And I certainly met the wrong brothers and sisters,' I finished, stating the obvious.

'Rhodes!' the Lord of the Sewers suddenly bellowed, ignoring my terrified babble.

Rhodes? Hm, not a bad idea at all. No doubt these relations of mine with their piratical tendencies had boats of some kind, maybe little steamers fuelled by their personal bio-gas, of which they certainly had ample supplies, and we were about to weigh anchor, reach the sea by way of the sewage system and chug off on holiday in the direction of Rhodes. Their distinctly alarming remarks just now had only been clumsy jokes, both a greeting and a test of a newcomer's courage. That's the way pirates act. Wow, those stinkers had really had me worried . . .

The throng surrounding me with all the avidity of visitors to the Colosseum in days of old and glaring intently at me in spite of their total blindness began to part in the middle. A narrow passage gradually formed between the audience on the stone walkway. It began to dawn on me, as I observed this act of collective anticipation, that Rhodes was not the Mediterranean island with its aura of legend, or any other holiday destination either. 'Rhodes' must be beyond anything imaginable, just as certain things slumber behind the very last steely gates of the unconscious, things that even the producers of nightmare horror shows daren't stage. An uneasy whisper passed through the grubby throng, and a sinister shadow could now be seen at the end of the corridor it had opened up. This shadow came closer and closer, positively rolling down the corridor like a tide of something slimy, and its approach was accompanied by a terrifying stamping that seemed to make the whole place tremble.

Gradually a shapeless figure which towered at least a head above those surrounding it came into sight. There was something ox-like about its movements. Clumsily and with forceful impact the shadow marched on, and at every step it took its entire astonishing corpulence wobbled in slow motion, like waves of fat breaking. But darkness still concealed this monstrous giant, and I could only speculate about its true appearance.

The closer it came, the louder swelled the awe-inspiring murmur of the sewer-dwelling monsters, as if they themselves feared the spirit they had conjured up. Then it stepped out into the light, and if the morbid fascination exercised by this amazing creature hadn't taken hold of my entire being, I'd surely have fainted dead away. He was the biggest Red Persian male I had ever seen: a Titan, a dinosaur from that fabled world where you don't take precise notice of animals' dimensions. He had no eyes either, but in his case that was the literal truth. Both eyes had been put out by some monster even worse than himself. Instead of shrinking together, however, the edges of his eye sockets had grown farther apart, so that they looked like craters surrounded by harsh shadows on some eerie planet. The left corner of his mouth, distorted by a scar, was somewhere in the region of his cheekbone; a horrible operation of some kind, probably performed with a knife, had extended it towards his upper jaw. Consequently his lower jaw hung down, and his mouth, constantly open and producing torrents of saliva, showed teeth which were badly damaged but still looked as dangerous as a set of butcher's knives. His long Persian coat had large bare patches showing wrinkled skin, probably as the result of bad burns. Rhodes had obviously been the victim of the most barbaric ill-treatment ever suffered at the hands of the lowest species of animal on earth, a species which none the less for some mysterious reason always regards itself as the highest. All the same, the martyrdom he had suffered had not improved his character. Instead of adopting the attitude of a tolerant pacifist, he preferred the silent role of executioner. For if this mountain of flesh, with his powerful pong, who was obviously barking mad and had all the charm of a bulldozer – if he wasn't an ice-cold killer then I was a white poodle with its arse shaved bare.

Rhodes strode all the way down the passage left free for him, displaying more and more of the horrible details of his many deformities as he did so, and finally he stopped in front of me. His clumsy halt made the fatty tissue of his walrus-like body ripple wildly one last time, like foaming waves breaking on the rocks. Now I was gazing straight into the black holes in the flesh of his wrecked face. They looked like prehistoric tombs, like chasms which seemed to suck my whole mind into them. At the same time I felt almost as if I were admiring a ruined cathedral from the vantage point of a small tourist, which in a crazy sort of way I was.

'Take a good look at what human beings have made of him!' said the big boss. Only minutes before I'd thought his own appearance couldn't be surpassed for horror, but now, by comparison with the mammoth confronting me, he looked like a cuddly stuffed toy on children's TV.

'And look at what they have made of us. We can't see any more, sad to say, but you don't need eyes to know that the most violent animals in the world are not lions or cheetahs. So perhaps you can understand why we must use every means we can to keep them from discovering us. Take a good look at him, my friend, because I'm afraid he's the last thing you will ever see.'

So these guys really meant it seriously. In that case, what was the point of crouching here in fright? They were going to murder me anyway. But to die unresisting, accepting my own execution meekly and in fear – that would be a real disgrace, unworthy of a Francis. No, I'd die like a man with nuts, good hard ones, not a trembling coward whose last act of aggression was to fire off a fart to sour earth's atmosphere. And if you looked at it realistically, the cards weren't stacked too badly against me. After all, this lot were blind, and an unexpectedly bold reaction on my part might well send them scattering in confusion. Moreover, I might not be up to their own level of bloodlust, but I was certainly more athletic than they were. They bore the marks of many diseases and ailments; a number of them were overweight from eating a poor, unbalanced diet, and where speed of reaction was concerned, the majority would have great difficulty in competing with my own hyper-sharp senses. See it in the proper light, and I really had just one ridiculous little disadvantage: there was only one of me, and – how many? – perhaps a thousand of them.

At least, however, I now knew how to save my skin. It would be cruel, but they left me no choice . . .

'Your time has come, little one,' said the chieftain, with grave dignity. 'You'd better close your eyes. It'll be easier that way, believe me. And as you were saying yourself just now, goodbye, stranger, we shall meet in heaven!'

A nasty smile crossed the Persian's distorted face, as if he'd been given permission to eat the whole birthday cake all by himself, and he bent a little way down to me. He seemed quite unaware of the time-honoured custom whereby our kind must go through a number of ritual moves such as aggressive hissing, tail-lashing, full frontal staring and whisker-bristling before launching into the attack. Instead, he did something which pointed the way, like a red arrow, straight to his Achilles heel. He swung his front leg and struck the left side of my head with his paw. I guessed that this strange move was not a bold challenge, but was made for a very simple reason: as Rhodes was blind, and in such bad condition that he had probably lost much of his sense of direction, he was using this trick to discover exactly where his opponent stood. He would simply deliver a sweeping blow in that opponent's general direction at first, and if his paw made contact he would know where his enemy was. Then he could wade in. The manoeuvre looked a bit like the way we 'play' with mice before dispatching them, a procedure humans find distasteful. The lords of creation forget that our original source of nourishment consisted of rats, relatively large prey animals equipped with dangerous teeth, so we needed to harry them until they were unconscious. Unfortunately these rough tactics have been extended to the relatively risk-free hunting of mice.

'Don't worry, mate!' croaked Rhodes in a hoarse, rusty voice after delivering his blow. It sounded as if his vocal cords were made of old iron. 'You won't feel a thing.'

He obviously intended to slit my throat.

'Do that again and I'll murder you!' I promised.

The audience gasped. Defying Rhodes was clearly next to blasphemy. Out of the corner of my eye I noticed the lips of Big Daddy Golden Earring curl into a pleased smile. He was rather enjoying this dubious show, though he seemed to have no doubt of its outcome. So far as Rhodes personally was concerned, he simply had not reckoned on such a development. He was a picture of total bewilderment. He was growling with a mixture of scorn and disbelief, but now and then he stopped for a moment and looked baffled, as if he were trying his hardest to make sense of my challenge. Then he shook his head vigorously again, which suggested that his attempts had led nowhere, and uttered another booming laugh.

'Murder me, will you, my friend?' he finally snarled with all the superiority of the sole of a shoe poised to squash a black beetle. The audience was now holding its breath. 'It'll be pretty strenuous. Bring you out in a sweat, you know.' With which he struck me on the head again with his other paw, this time hard enough to hurt, and with his claws out. They left a deep scratch in my right ear. Blood welled out of it.

I unsheathed the claws of my own forepaw, went like lightning for his empty left eye socket and drove my claws through the rubbery flesh. When they reached the brain I turned them into deadly hooks. Rhodes's slack lower jaw dropped a little further; his water-melon of a head shook in my grip like a kettle boiling dry just before it explodes, and a jet of blood shot from his nostrils. Then I withdrew my claws, and he slumped to the ground like a shot elephant. As he fell he uttered a blood-curdling howl which echoed on and on in that stony labyrinth. It sounded like a train of tanker trucks going over the edge of a precipice and slowly falling apart to the sound of metallic screeching.

'Ooooooooooooh!' went the crowd around us, striking up a chorus fit to make your flesh creep, as if the last agony of Rhodes were being telepathically transferred to their own nervous systems. There was awe at the moment of release rather than sympathy for the dying Rhodes in that cry; it suggested an unsettling affinity with the liberating power of death, and struck a hidden chord in me too. They couldn't actually watch me deal the mortal blow, but they all seemed to feel that Rhodes was lost for ever as executioner in the Catacombs of Mercy.

His penetrating howl became a miserable wheeze, and the wheeze finally dwindled to a despairing moan which echoed for a little longer and then died away entirely. His head dropped to one side and he breathed his last. I looked at the lifeless colossus with pity. Pangs of conscience began to set in. Against the background of the gently flowing stream, he now looked the very image of a fat man taking an afternoon nap on the beach. Rhodes lay on his back, all four paws outstretched, and but for the thin trickle of blood under his nose you might indeed have thought he was asleep. This was the second corpse I'd seen in under an hour. However, whatever I did I mustn't let my scruples show, not unless I wanted to undermine the credibility of my ice-cold Mickey Rourke act.

'Well, I said I'd murder him if he did that again,' I remarked in bored tones, turning to my audience. 'Anyone else fancy a bout?'

While the others were still open-mouthed and busy trying to recover from their astonishment, the Oriental lady, who had taken cover behind the boss when Rhodes appeared, shot out again. For a moment I thought I was going to have to tackle this termagant too, and largish cracks appeared in the cool façade I was maintaining with some difficulty. However, the all-clear sounded when Naomi Campbell in furs raced past me and began sniffing hard at the corpse. Then she laid her head against his belly, which towered up like a sand dune, and listened. The diagnosis was obviously not what she'd expected.

'He's killed him!' she cried. 'The shit! He really has, he's finished Rhodes off!'

Clearly this was more than she could understand, and she was unable to stop weeping and wailing over what couldn't be undone now. The rest of the mob joined her lamentations, uttering curses and loud, confused expressions of dismay, and competing with each other in suggesting suitable reprisals. As they did so they nodded their heads in time again. Finally the boss felt impelled to rise from his place, with the morose bearing of a small-town judge sick and tired of the squabbles of the local gentry, and uttered a welcome cry of, 'Shut your mouths, will you?' This duly took effect, suddenly silencing the mob which had been thirsting to lynch me. There was an oppressive stillness, broken only by the scratching of claws on the stony ground as the patriarch slowly made his way over to the scene of the crime.

'You've got us into a nice mess now, little one,' he said rather sadly, as he ceremoniously inspected the corpse with his nose.

'Well, if I hadn't, he'd have made *me* into a nice mess!' I defended myself. 'And you should really be grateful to me.

There's your breakfast at last. Ought to be enough for everyone, and you can keep me for harvest festival or whatever.'

'What the hell are you talking about? One of those clever-dicks who think their powers of deduction something marvellous, are you? You won't do much more thinking when your head's jammed up your arse. Maybe you're smart enough to snuff out a poor old sod who could hardly stand on his feet, but do you think you can put on the same show with every single one of us?'

'I kind of thought we might stop for the regulation breaks between rounds.'

'The death penalty, that's what I say!' screeched Lady Boss, and her claws shot past my nose just a hair's breadth away. 'Let's kill the bastard now, before he can do any more harm.'

'Gently, gently,' Golden Earring soothed her. 'Up to this point we just had a troublesome witness, and we were going to deal with him painlessly. The situation's quite different now. We now have before us someone who's sent one of ourselves across the Jordan. So his death must be celebrated with all due ceremony, if only in honour of the memory of Rhodes. What's your name, then, little fellow?'

'Francis,' I said.

The wiry witch froze in the middle of her nervous movements. The Chartreux suddenly raised his head, and he too remained perfectly still in that posture. An excited whispering arose from the middle of the assembled company and spread like the wind to its farthest corners. After a while His Majesty, obviously partaking of the confusion felt by his companions in misfortune, began on a series of what they call displacement activities. He licked the root of his tail like one possessed, scratched vigorously behind his ears, and paid great attention to washing his balls. We perform these displacement activities spontaneously when we have to make a difficult decision or size up some unusual situation.

Human beings perform various displacement activities too, without being aware of it: for instance, when they're in some kind of difficulty they will rub their ears, massage their foreheads as if in pain, make acrobatic movements of the tongue outside the mouth, and last but not least they go in for smoking, smoking and more smoking.

'Francis?' said the leader, more to himself than to me. 'You don't mean the Francis?'

'Well, I'm not the sailor or the film director. Just Francis,' I said, shrugging my shoulders. Maybe they were thinking of some particular brand of tinned food.

'The Francis who solved the most complicated crime ever to take place in our ranks? The Francis whose deeds are legendary? Francis the genius?'

'There was certainly a dark period in my past when I encountered a lord of darkness who had forgotten that light could ever exist. Compared to you lot, though, he suddenly seems about as diabolical as one of Steffi Graf's ball-boys.'

'Why didn't you tell us at once?'

'I hate personality cults – particularly when the idea of the cult is to eat the personality.'

'I'm afraid you've got quite the wrong impression of our community, Francis. I suppose it's partly our own fault. Still, since we met in such unfortunate circumstances you were bound to misunderstand certain things, including our real nature. If you're to get the true picture we shall have to tell you a long story. Allow me to introduce myself: my name is Saffron.'

'And yours is Cardamom, right?' I said, turning to the warrior queen beside me. She didn't seem at all keen on the idea of making peace, far from it: it was more as if the revelation of my name had spoiled the game for her. She moved her head back and forth suspiciously, ready to strike again at any moment, eyes narrowed to slits, and performed an orientation manoeuvre to make sure she could still locate my exact position. To this end she employed the radar effect of her vibrating whiskers, which can register even the smallest changes in air circulation. When she 'read off' the results, they provided her spatial imagination with a three-dimensional diagram of the object of her interest. It was almost like seeing without eyes.

'Wrong, Sherlock. Niger, that's my name. I was once called Cindy like that man's daughter – the girl who wanted something cuddly for Christmas. She lost interest in me on Boxing Day, so the man put me in a plastic bag and threw me in the river. Luckily the bag was torn, and I managed to swim to the bank and hide in a drainpipe. But you needn't think I decided to take the name of Niger so as to identify with an underprivileged race of humans. It was just because the name suits me, being the Latin word for . . . '

'Black,' I said.

'Yes, well, goes to show you deserve your reputation as a clever-dick,' Saffron interrupted. 'Hostilities over now, right? We've been waiting a long time for someone like you. You see, we have a job for you, Francis.'

'A job? Look, I'm sorry, Your Highness, but I gave up detecting ages ago. The only cases now solved by yours truly Mr Marlowe concern the mysterious disappearance of smoked salmon from the larder.'

'That's OK; we don't want you to solve a case, we want you to find someone. But before we go into detail there's a final ceremony I think we should perform.'

Before I could protest and assure them that all I intended to find was the goddam exit from this damp realm of shadows, Saffron approached the corpse of Rhodes, raised his head to the vault above and intoned our familiar and musical 'Yeeeoooowl!' This time that mysterious cry lasted longer than the usual short burst, because it was taken up by the blind animals encircling us as if they were singing a round and went on and on, becoming an endless lament. If one of the singers struck up a sequence of notes but had to stop for breath, his neighbour stepped into the breach. It was like a musical relay. They wove a moving tapestry of sound which finally dissolved entirely into the shrill howls peculiar to us, which we utter when we're particularly excited. No doubt about it, they were howling a funeral dirge, a requiem for one of our own kind, and one I had killed.

Saffron lowered his head and gave Rhodes a gentle push with his nose. As if this were only a symbolic gesture, like a politician laying a wreath, several of his subjects came up from various directions and pushed the dead body on before them with their own noses. The corpse rolled over the ground, and was finally tipped over the side of the stone walkway to fall into the sewer. 'Yeeeoooowl!' sang his blind friends, bidding farewell to their companion for the last time as Rhodes floated away downstream like a rudderless raft, and although I had a lump in my own throat by now I sang along with them as loud as I could.

'It wasn't your fault, Francis,' said Saffron quietly. 'Or rather, we're all equally guilty. Rhodes certainly had more blood on his paws than you'd find on Charles Manson's hands. His IQ didn't exactly qualify for the *Guinness Book of Records*, and we found he came in handy to do the rough stuff. He'd probably have died of his injuries and deformities in a few weeks' time anyway. However, we must justify ourselves before God, even for the death of such a bloodthirsty being. Why, I ask myself, is our species doomed to show hostility, indeed brute force, when it encounters strangers of its own kind? Is it because of our origins – because we were once hunters in vast territories where a single competitor could endanger our survival? No, clever scientific arguments don't really explain anything. Misunderstandings, misunderstandings! And always violence. Yes, violence seems to be in our nature.'

Once the mourners, tears in their eyes, had dispatched

their defunct Angel of Death into the maw of the sewers they formed a dense crowd around us again. I felt a vague excitement rising among them, as if some pleasing event were about to take place. I had lost sight of Niger during the funeral ceremony, but now she pushed her way out of the crowd again and made straight for Saffron.

'Scout come back?' he asked when she was beside him.

'Yes, it's main inlet number thirty-four this time, over to the west of the city. They've finished the repair works at number seventy-eight and sealed it off again.'

'Then we have quite a way to go. You come too, Francis, and *en route* I'll tell you why you mustn't refuse our request.'

'But can't we discuss it here, Saffron? Where are we going?'

'From darkness into light – for the sake of our health.'

And saying no more, he set off at a determined trot. As if all the rest were just waiting for that signal to start, total chaos broke out among the company, who had hitherto displayed all the exemplary discipline of consumers queuing outside food shops in the former Communist countries. Instantly some of the blind animals leaped over our heads, like salmon going upstream, to get a front place in the mad rush, and there was much excited pushing and shoving on the path, which was far too narrow for such a crowd. It was as if a fire had broken out near by. However, theirs was a cheerful excitement motivated solely by anticipation, so in spite of everything courtesy and consideration were the order of the day. Everyone made sure no one else got shoved too hard or came too close to the left-hand side of the walkway, where you might get pushed off into the sewer. Above all, they took the greatest care of the babies who made up a kind of fluffily mobile substructure in this milling throng. I could account for the sudden restlessness of my blind acquaintances only by assuming that there was a prospect of some reservoir of food in the distance.

Saffron, Niger and I had soon dropped back to the rear of

the column, a place the boss obviously found congenial; it meant he could start on his story in peace. By now I'd spent so much time in the dark that my optical sensitivity to light was at its highest, and I could make out the winding ways of the sewers more clearly. For instance, I was surprised to see, in the distance, a fork where three streams met and flowed into the tunnel where we now were. Three identical tunnels led from this fork to goodness knows where, and in their turn must branch off into several other winding tunnels, making the underground maze complete. I was beginning to realise that my original plan of getting out of this labyrinth under my own steam had been an illusion, and I'd never see the light of day again without the aid of my blind friends.

'I expect you're wondering why we're blind, Francis,' said Saffron reflectively as we trotted after the rest of the enthusiastic procession. Niger, pacing along at my left, was listening attentively, her head bent, although she must have known the story already. 'The answer's simple: we live permanently in the dark, so in the course of time our visual nerves atrophy and become useless. You might not think it, but we're happy to make that sacrifice if it spares us having to live with human beings. We've all enjoyed human hospitality in the past, you see. Even I did. My owner was a well-known painter, regarded as a tremendous aesthete in artistic circles. My twin brother and I were a finishing touch for the sinister décor of his flat – a kind of live eye-catching device. This artist went in for kinky leather and sado-masochistic sex, and he admired a slim figure. The mere sight of someone well-nourished made him feel quite ill. He sometimes starved us for days on end so that we'd live up to his physical ideal too. When he went away for a long weekend he usually left us locked in the flat, and on one of these weekends my brother died of thirst because our owner hadn't even left us a bowl of water. Another time he went on holiday to Egypt in search of inspiration, but the only inspiration he brought back came from the goddess Bast, whose statue wears earrings. He thought this was a brilliant idea, and pierced my own ears for rings the very next day. After that I could never scratch behind my ears again without catching my claws in the rings and making my ears bleed. I was a great hit at his parties, all the same. Then things got rather nasty: the artist suffered a creative block – or rather, to put it bluntly, he went off his head. To stimulate his imagination he started torturing me and observing my reactions. He enjoyed it. He always wore his leather outfit and mask for these sessions, using a fondue fork heated on the stove for his experiments. After one such orgy my wounds burned with such intolerable pain that I ran all over the flat howling, frantically looking for something to cool me down. In my desperation I finally jumped into the lavatory bowl, plunging my whole body head first in the water. It soothed my wounds and my other injuries, but next moment I realised I was stuck in the S-bend. I couldn't go on, and I couldn't go back – now what? But then I saw for the first time the advantages of the anorexia he'd forced on me. I felt sure I could squeeze on down that squalid outlet if I helped myself with my forepaws and didn't panic. Eventually, half drowned, I reached the main drain, and when someone up above flushed the cistern, the rush of water washed me right into the sewage system. Down here I soon found companions in misfortune who'd suffered a similar fate. I haven't been back to the world above since then.'

He'd put a bit of weight on since then too, I silently added. But I didn't feel at all like laughing. I'd always known what kind of things went on in the world beyond the safety of Gustav's four walls. I was only too well aware that humans published meticulous records of dreadful things done to my own kind in their media, and though they might shed crocodile tears about it over a good meal and a glass of expensive wine it was only symbolic, like turning a prayer mill. They kept quiet about the everyday torments inflicted on animals because no one was really interested. By now the awe-inspiring word 'creature' had become a term of abuse.

Meanwhile the procession had reached the place where the tunnels divided, and the blind animals were jumping the sewers in pairs, with artistic ease. As this astonishingly precise manoeuvre was performed at high speed and they jumped one after the other in rapid succession, it looked from a distance as if bridges were rippling up and down over the three streams, bridges whose colour was constantly changing. At the end of our path, a corner where two of the streams met at an acute angle, Saffron and Niger catapulted themselves upwards too, flew through the air with limbs outstretched, like bats, and landed on the other side with the elegance of griffins. Now that my turn had come, my admiration was tempered with sheer fright, because I suddenly realised that the distance across the sewer to the path on the opposite bank, which also started at an angle, was at least two and a half metres. It was very dark here too, which made calculating even the simplest jump more difficult. At the same time, however, I felt ashamed to be bringing up the rear, and after a moment's hesitation I finally imitated the others. As a result, I was literally left dangling: my forepaws came down on the other side according to plan, but my back paws hit the void. Flailing frantically, I tried to correct my error, and for a split second, as my claws touched the side of the walkway, I thought my awkward acrobatics would do the trick. However, they were sabotaged by the slime deposited on the stone. I slipped and fell in the sludgy water. Fortunately there was a kind of swimming-pool ladder close to the place where I'd had fallen in, so I was able to haul myself up by it, like a monster emerging from the lagoon. I thanked my stars no one could see me doing this slapstick act, because otherwise more than one revision to the legend of Teenage Mutant Ninja Francis would have been called for.

When we set off again, padding after the pack along

another nameless stone walkway, I fancied for a moment that even Saffron was wrinkling his nose. I shook myself as if a thousand fleas were attacking me, because the unique smell of the water in my fur after my bath caused deep offence to my already pretty paranoid obsession with cleanliness. I kept stopping, licking my coat frantically and combing my fur with my teeth to remove small lumps. The thought of the unspeakable substances I was swallowing in the process made my stomach churn. While I was trying to get perfectly clean and keep up with the others at the same time, Niger took up the story.

'We represent the conscience of our species, Francis,' she said belligerently. 'Even more: we grant final asylum, the last refuge from torture and death. For we are the Company of the Merciful. You see, Francis, the inequality that divides human beings into children of fortune and poor unlucky sods doesn't stop at them; it affects animals too. Though it's worth wondering whether the thoroughbred Arab in the royal stud who's had a dozen operations on his legs since falling in the Derby is really any better off than a forest squirrel facing hunger daily. Alas, we're all equal in suffering. You've seen nothing but the chocolate-covered side of life so far, Francis. But not many of us lie about on velvet cushions dozing ourselves blotto in sunny conservatories. Not many of us can afford to philosophise about the ideal ingredients of tinned food. You may think Saffron's escape down the S-bend sounds particularly tricky, but humans themselves sometimes use that way of getting rid of pets when they're not wanted any more, or there are too many of them. Drowning a whole litter in the bath is something that practical, inventive humans find rather unpleasant today, so they may just dispose of the little ones down the loo – painlessly, they think. After a nightmare journey through the drainage system, the babies reach us and we give them another chance of life – those who haven't drowned already.

Or sometimes humans breed us into weird-looking specimens prized only for their extravagant deformities, like our unfortunate relatives of the hairless Sphynx breed, and individuals who don't fit the breeding programme get thrown into the dustbin half dead. Some of these victims, though badly injured, just manage to escape from their stinking coffins with the last of their strength, and then they find their way down to us through the gratings over gutters in the street. Living in the dark all the time has made us infertile, and we can't have children of our own. So instead we take great care of the children we've adopted and of our older brothers and sisters from the vivisection laboratories. They can spend the evening of their days peacefully here in the catacombs. The greatest risk we run is discovery by the sewage workers. They'd report their amazing find to the powers that be at once, and the powers that be would feel obliged to carry out a rigorous cleansing operation. We eat rats; luckily humans haven't found any foolproof way of exterminating rats yet. Hunting them is quite dangerous and sometimes leads to bloodshed, because they've grown abnormally large and heavy in the Promised Land of the sewers. But all things considered we can feel quite pleased with the success of our mission – or we could if sinister shadows from the past hadn't surfaced a little while back . . . '

'Shadows from the past?' I said, surprised. This whole story had sounded like the last word in horror: could there be worse to come?

'That's what you could call them,' Saffron growled, taking up the tale. The column of greyish backs and expectantly raised tails winding on ahead of us curved round to the right.

'There was only one shadow really. But of course the past is interesting mainly as it affects the present. I believe you encountered something strange soon after entering our territory, Francis.'

'One corpse, drowned. Probably European Shorthair.

Head severed from neck and no longer present. Numerous very large bite-marks on the body. Had probably been in the water for several days, hence the extremely bloated appearance of the body. Is to be assumed that the killing was not preceded by a fight of the sort usual among us with its rituals of challenge and defence; killer did not employ the customary neck-bite. Conclusion: victim must have been in a state of shock at the time, rendering him unable to defend himself and making things easy for the murderer. The extent of the brutality can hardly be explained any other way.'

I thought, with some pride, that no expert in forensic medicine could have put the salient points better. Saffron and Niger seemed impressed by my lightning analysis too, and momentarily slowed down. However, the big boss wasn't going to show his respect for my little grey cells openly. He wouldn't want anyone encroaching on his own authority. So he just looked impassive.

'We guessed it was something like that,' he said gruffly, following up his remark with a mock yawn. 'However, you weren't to know that this was the fifteenth or twentieth corpse to have paid us a visit to date.'

Dread descended on me like black folds of mourning tulle. I thought I was going to stumble, because the horror of it temporarily made me lose my balance. Good God, what monster was working at this frenzied rate to prove his skill in butchery? What could the motive be? Sheer love of violence? Hunger? Madness?

'The twentieth corpse?' I murmured incredulously. Something inside me refused to believe the inconceivable.

'Or maybe the thirtieth. We stopped counting the mutilated bodies after a while.' Saffron was gradually forgetting to play the authority game; he sounded genuinely upset. His expression and the thoughtful way he walked showed that these incidents got right under his fur. In fact he was very worried indeed.

'Because of our living conditions here, we can't help swimming in the sewers now and then. I know humans think we avoid ordinary water the way the devil avoids the holy variety, but that's not true of all of us – much of it's based on superstition, and practice can make anyone a good swimmer. Anyway, recently we've found that when we go into the water we're more and more likely to find one of these mutilated corpses floating into our paws. We believe the murders are committed somewhere in the forest outside the city, because we quite often find pine needles stuck in the victims' wounds. There are some streams and ditches there which run straight into the sewage system. And the nearby farms have drainage feeding into the system too. So it's possible the murder victims were brothers and sisters of ours living with farmers in the country.'

'And you want me to go out into the world and discover who dunnit?' I said, without much enthusiasm.

'Oh no, you don't need to do anything like that, my dear Francis. We know who dunnit.'

'You know who . . . but then for heaven's sake why don't you get your skates on and pick him up?'

I stopped abruptly. I wished I hadn't made that last remark. Sometimes, I realised, I had all the sensitivity of a slogger in a baseball game.

'Your eyes,' I said, awkwardly. 'I suppose they make things difficult for you outside.'

'Yes, there's a bit of a problem there,' said Saffron, to my relief ignoring the brick I'd dropped. 'But the complicated part is finding him, because he's everywhere and nowhere. In fact strictly speaking he doesn't exist: he's a legend, a shadow from the past . . . '

Saffron suddenly stopped and sat there, concentrating hard. The sparkling gold rings swung gently from his pointed ears, pricked in their most receptive position; his head swayed back and forth like a tank turret seeking its target, and his whiskers quivered busily, as if they were insect antennae processing information. Then his blind, flickering gaze came to rest on a certain point in the waters of the sewer.

'Niger, you tell him about the Black Knight,' whispered the Chartreux, barely audibly, and with a mighty leap he plunged head first into the water. While I was still trying to recover from my surprise, he came to the surface again with something struggling frantically between his teeth. He had obviously caught a rat and was taming it for breakfast. I'd already heard amazing tales of the acoustic sensitivity of the blind, but this episode surely took the biscuit.

Paying no further attention to the incident, Niger walked on. I took this as an invitation to follow her. Leaving the angler to his hobby, I followed close on my companion's heels. Naturally I couldn't resist the temptation to cast several glances back over my shoulder for a better view of Saffron's extraordinary activities, but I couldn't really see much except a frantic splashing as either the hunter tried to drag his prey under water or vice versa.

'Once upon a time, Francis, something evil ruled the underworld.' Niger closed her eyes and stretched her neck telescopically forward, as if passing through an imaginary wall into the realm of the past. Inexpressible horrors seemed to be resurrected before her mind's eye.

'We didn't know what the evil thing was, but we knew it was *there*. Anyway, it seemed to be a creature of darkness, like us, and it could come round the corner without warning any time it liked. When it did appear, sudden as a jack-in-the-box, it would grab one of us and make mincemeat of him in the fraction of a second. We usually panicked and ran for our lives. If some brave person did go to the victim's aid, he'd be mincemeat too in no time at all, leaving only a couple of extremities, torn off but despised by the phantom, to bear witness to his courage. Our enemy was bestiality incarnate and completely unpredictable, and as time went on it became a terrible scourge threatening to wipe us all out. We crept along, hugging the walls, our teeth chattering; we couldn't hunt properly because there was no way to turn the threat aside, and we saw a time coming when we'd be wiped out. Meanwhile, the phantom was pursuing its annihilation programme as relentlessly as a finely calibrated circular saw, always trusting to vicious surprise attacks. Sometimes it would lie in wait in a secret niche above the wall, leap down on any group of brothers and sisters who happened to be passing and wreak indescribable havoc among them. Or it would dart out of a branch drainpipe like a combine harvester run amok and dispose of one of us with only a couple of bites. Whenever these things happened we heard terrible screams which sounded like the dreadful howling of madmen unable to express the infinite horror of their dark, imaginary world in language. And we heard echoes of terrifying sounds: the hiss of fangs plunged into live flesh, the dry crack of bones, the smacking of lips – oh, that disgusting lip-smacking sound which conveyed supreme contempt!'

Niger stopped, and a surreptitious glance showed me that tears had gathered in her eyes which, though blind, were as lovely as fjords surrounded by the mist. The horror seemed to have etched itself permanently into her memory, and like most witnesses of violent events she kept going back over the hell she'd suffered. I wanted to say something comforting, but I felt next moment that would be a clumsy, useless thing to do. I couldn't comfort someone whose suffering I hadn't shared.

Unexpectedly, Saffron caught up with us. He was wet through, and in his mouth he carried the fattest, ugliest rat I had ever seen. To be honest, I hadn't got to know very many of these unattractive contemporaries of ours to date, certainly none who had swollen to twice their normal size by lurking in subterranean vaults. For the rat Saffron was carrying in his teeth like a retriever was more the size of a stout rabbit. The hunter himself bore his trophy as casually as if he'd just stopped off at the supermarket meat counter. It had several deep bites disfiguring the neck area.

'Hab you tol hib bou Cazy Uo?' he mumbled, since the prey in his mouth made it impossible for him to articulate clearly. The rat's dead, open eyes stared sideways and accusingly at me, as if reproaching me for hanging about in such disreputable company.

'I was just coming to that part,' said Niger, suppressing a sob and shaking her head violently to get rid of the tears.

'Hugo grew up during this bad time. He was a Tiffany, a long-haired Burmese: silky, sable-brown fur, very long and hopelessly tangled; eyes which might have been cast in high-carat gold, bushy tail, muscular build, round head. He was in a pitiful state when he was washed down into the sewers. That soon changed, and we very quickly realised that not only was he the most handsome young male we'd ever reared, he was also, extraordinarily, the only one of us to retain his vision. But it soon turned out that he suffered from severe behavioural disorders. With Hugo, even childish games quickly became so rough that his surprised companions were left with nasty injuries. When he grew older he would pick on anyone, even his foster mother, and in fact he hurt her quite badly. And he spent less and less time with us; he became a recluse, turning up only to pick violent quarrels. One day he broke our taboo: he actually killed one of us in a fight. We expelled him from our community as punishment for the crime, and thereafter we knew him only as Crazy Hugo. Like the evil phantom, he assumed the aura of a ghost who seldom appeared, but whose watchful eyes were secretly observing us all the time. After a while, however, we began to forget Crazy Hugo, being too busy with our own troubles. In fact the one we had cast out actually became a legendary figure of whom we told the most amazing tales with paws before our mouths.

'One day – by this time our numbers were much reduced by the monster's terrorist attacks – we were out hunting and came to a part of the sewage system where we'd never been before. As we went further and further on we suddenly came up against a wall, and realised too late that it was a blind alley. But by then we were in the trap, for at that moment we heard the dreadful dragging noise the phantom made. It had obviously been following us the whole way there. Now it took up its position behind us, cutting off the only way of escape. We were at its mercy. It just stood there, patiently waiting to turn our flesh and bones to bloody mush with its murderous jaws. And the descriptions the young ones and children who could still see gave us at last revealed the secret of its identity.'

'Some crazy human being, right?' I guessed astutely.

Saffron dropped the stinking rat from his mouth and with a mighty blow of his paw kicked it to the right, into an alcove where a stone had fallen out of the wall.

'Wrong. It was a dog!' he said, immediately raising his head and sniffing hard, as if he'd picked up a new scent. I had been so spellbound by Niger's story that only now did I notice the glittering megabeam of light, suggesting the dazzling effect of a UFO landing, which penetrated a gap in the roof far ahead. Surprises were coming thick and fast. The pack in front of us sprinted forward towards the light which apparently represented salvation, while we three went on walking at a leisurely pace.

'Yes, it was a bloody great dog, a huge black mastiff,' Niger went on. 'In normal circumstances – whatever normal circumstances may be – we'd have felt sorry for him, because like us he was obviously an outcast, only trying to satisfy his hunger. And like us, he clearly preferred this paw-to-mouth existence to the company of human beings. Humans regard dogs like him only as their servants. But in our present situation, as I was saying, we could hardly afford solidarity. This dog was our enemy, a monster, and within a few seconds he was going to tear us all to bits, as sure as the hypocritical Amen they say in human churches. He took a few steps towards us and we flinched back in alarm. But next moment we heard a miserable howling. It undoubtedly came from the mastiff; it was just too dog-like a noise for any of us to have made it. We quickly got the sighted children to tell us what was going on. Crazy Hugo had suddenly shot out of the darkness and gone for the dog's throat like a flying vampire. He must have been shadowing us the whole time, and when he guessed we were in real danger he attacked. Anyway, the dog had no chance at all to do anything about Hugo, who clung to his throat however much he twisted and turned in unbearable agony. Finally the crazy creature drove his incisors deep into the crazy dog's oesophagus until the latter fell down, unable to do anything but whine miserably. We were praying Hugo would keep going and slaughter him with the same barbaric tortures we'd suffered ourselves. Let him know fear, the real fear of death, before he finally received the *coup de grâce*! Instead, a very strange thing happened. It must have been something to do with kindred spirits being on the same wavelength. The dog was wheezing as if begging for mercy. He'd surrendered ages ago, because Hugo was clinging to his vital artery like a malevolent leech; the smallest movement of resistance would mean the mastiff's dispatch. At long last the dragon had found a knight who was a match for him. Then, we were told, their eyes met in an exchange of glances quite different from the usual hostile staring that goes on between victor and vanquished. It was a current of recognition, of understanding for the terrible things they had done, each of them seeing his own reflection in his enemy's face. It was the merging of two forms of madness into a single and even more monstrous derangement. For some inexplicable reason Crazy Hugo had saved us, delivering us from the curse that threatened to wipe us out. But with that act he'd finally sold the soul which had still been related to ours up till then. He'd entered into a kind of pact with the devil. He let go of the mastiff, who got to his feet despite his injuries and looked at his conqueror as if hypnotised. Then Hugo mounted his dragon and trotted away on him like a cowboy riding into the sunset. We've never met either of them since, but they still live on in our legends.'[7]

'No, we've never met the two of them again, but we've heard some strange stories about them on occasion.' Saffron stopped, licked his forepaw thoughtfully and then rubbed it over his head. He seemed to be remembering that period with horror too.

'You think they did the murders?' I asked, not that I really wanted to know the details. Well, why shouldn't the theory of a crazy dog and an even crazier Hugo committing serial murder be true? By now, after all the amazing things I'd learnt in the last few minutes, I was ready to believe in the existence of the Seven Dwarfs themselves.

'Not a lot of outside news makes its way down here.' Saffron set off again, and Niger and I followed him towards the place which was illuminated as if in a floodlight. The others were just beginning to reach it. 'But we've heard that Hugo and his murderous steed have left the sewage system for good and are now terrorising the forest near by. People there call him the Black Knight because on his infrequent but spectacular appearances he's always seen riding that crazy dog. They say he sits upright on the mastiff like a human horseman, and the sight of the couple always strikes mystical awe into observers. They're the ultimate outsiders, so it seems logical for them to persecute those who live comfortably in the safety of human homes. Solitude and the outlaw life have finally brutalised them, and now they kill just out of hatred and envy – let alone the fact that they're totally deranged, of course.'

'The monstrous extent of the violence certainly supports that theory,' I agreed. 'It more or less rules out a single perpetrator. But what makes you so sure this particular pair are the murderers?'

'Well, we can't imagine who else in the animal kingdom would be responsible for such horrors. Besides, the crimes bear the trademarks we know from the past.'

'Oh, great. So what am I supposed to do if I catch Hugo and his lovely companion in the act? Put the handcuffs on and cart them off to the police station?'

'Just come back here and tell us where they're hiding out. We'll do the rest. Our situation now is very different from what it was before. There are more of us than there used to be, and we have far more hunting experience. But first, some brave and enterprising character has to go out and get us precise information on their whereabouts. We made a big mistake when we let those two go. It was irresponsible of us. Now they're at large out there, like psychopath chainsaw killers in a movie, inflicting dreadful carnage on the rural population. You must find the Black Knight, Francis. He's a disgrace to our kind, a festering sore that must be burnt out as soon as possible.'

Well roared, lion! But how exactly did Saffron envisage all this? I'd be useless at reading tracks North American Indian fashion, and I wasn't linked up to any reconnaissance satellites either. To make matters even more dicey, all I knew of wildernesses, to be honest, came out of a TV series based on the Leatherstocking tales. I knew the difference between a bush and a tree all right, but the mere thought of a forest jam-packed with bushes and trees made me feel like Hansel and Gretel rolled into one. Anyway, how did we know the murders actually had been committed by these two double-dyed villains? OK, so the vicious mutilation of the corpses fitted certain aspects of the murderer's profile as described, but there were other mad folk around too. If you read the papers as regularly as I did, you might well think the whole world was one vast funny farm. In view of these and similar considerations, I finally came to what seemed to me a brilliant conclusion. I'd promise the blind folk the help of my detective abilities, but once I was out of here I'd run straight to the nearest emergency call-box and vandalise it until a police patrol came to my aid, identified me from the tattoo on my rump and carted me back to my beloved Gustav. I'm ashamed to say I was even quite looking forward to seeing Francesca.

To my relief, solemn oaths and so forth didn't seem to be on the agenda. My companions were getting more and more taciturn as we approached the bright circle of light. Stealthily prowling forward, they were getting into a state very familiar to me: eyes narrowed, heads pointed forward into furry ovals, fur itself velvety as if it had been well shampooed. However, this change in them with all its pleasing concomitant phenomena wasn't because they expected petting. No, the cause of their abrupt switch into a trance-like state was the anticipation of something without which our kind would perish miserably: sunlight! But hadn't Saffron said they were blind because they always lived in the dark? Some kind of explanation was in order.

We soon caught up with the others, who were standing motionless, pressed close together, in the man-made crater and letting the dazzling rays of the morning sun shine through them. They all kept their eyes closed, and they seemed more rapt than ever, as if someone had cast a magic spell on them. I felt a sudden sense of happiness myself at seeing the bright sky above me again and feeling pleasant warmth on my coat after so many hours in the dark. I discovered later that we had made pilgrimage to a building site at a main inlet, where the effluent draining away from a whole part of town was diverted into the various branches of the sewage system. Basically, the place was a circular shaft lined with concrete, wide in diameter and deep enough to make you dizzy. There were building tools everywhere: bottles of gas for welding and any amount of steel and wood. The workers must have stopped for their tea break. The sun stood right above this chasm, giving optimum radiation. After the ceremony Saffron told me that the blind community sought out such open building sites once a day when human beings didn't happen to be around, so that they could tank up with energy from the rays of the sun. Even spirits of darkness can't do without the essential life-giving elixir of daylight. So that explained why my brothers and sisters living underground were spared rickets.

However, they displayed some macabre differences from us ordinary mortals when it came to sunbathing. The reason why the blind folk kept their eyes closed in the sun must have been that their atrophied visual nerves would feel dreadful pain at any contact with bright light. But they had also made a solemn, even religious rite out of the absorption of Vitamin D, something we sighted animals take in as we roll on the ground. When Saffron, Niger and I had thrust our way to the centre of the worshippers – a bird's-eye view of them would have given the impression of a sombre patchwork quilt – a very odd thing happened. As if a signal had been given they struck up their shrill 'Yeeeoooowl!' again, first softly, then louder and louder, until the yowling culminated in a symphonic hurricane. At the climax of this happy caterwauling they raised their forepaws, stood on their hind legs and stretched their bodies up, so that they looked like dogs begging. Then they all opened their eyes at the same moment. The glaring light, which must have felt like spurting acid as it fell on their retinas, sent stabbing pains through them, and the emotional 'Yeeeeoooowl!' took on a primeval note that went to the heart. Only now did I understand the full meaning of that cry. Saffron and his people had as close a relationship with the phenomenon of pain as bats with the echo phenomenon. They had suffered violence from youth; their basic experiences as children were not of pleasure but of pain and despair. Even later, down here in the sewers, they hadn't found the salvation they hoped for: theirs was a hard and painful existence. They had to get their food with great difficulty and danger; they had to put up with dirt, disease, crippling injuries and the eternal darkness, and then the monster who persecuted them had taught them the meaning of mortal fear and pain all over again. Their whole existence was bound up with constant pain, which gradually became an essential part of their emotional life and finally a ritual compulsion. Every day they made their way to some place where the sunlight they needed could penetrate, and let it shine on their coats. But necessity had combined with perversion in an extraordinary way, finally degenerating into this grotesque ceremony. It was if they were sacrificing to the god of pain by exposing their most vulnerable parts, their damaged eyes, in an attempt to placate him. They were torturing themselves of their own free will, because a life without pain seemed to be more than they could comprehend.

For a moment it occurred to me that they might have been telling me a pack of lies in their tale of Hugo & Co. Could be they'd committed the crimes themselves, those crimes representing the worst pain they could devise, and I was being asked to spread the story of the Black Knight among our kind outside just to divert suspicion from the real murderers. The Company of the Merciful was to figure as a league of high-minded chivalry, not a bunch of lunatics given to such excesses of violence that they sometimes went right over the top and killed one of their own species. Because look at it soberly, and there was something ludicrous about the idea of a small Sherlock Holmes tracking down two monsters in the wilderness – while at the same time it would be very good PR work for my sewer-dwelling friends.

In spite of these suspicions I dismissed all doubts for the

time being. The present atmosphere made clear thinking impossible. By now I was in the grip of religious enthusiasm myself, carried away by the song of suffering which was a musical equivalent of weeping. Finally I got up on my own hind legs, stretched, waved my forepaws ecstatically in the air and wailed in a voice choked with tears: 'Yeeeeooowl! Yeeeeooowl! Yeeeeooowl!'

This strange performance lasted about ten minutes, and was abruptly ended by the approach of the first construction worker. The blind folk retreated into the sewers and then, to my surprise, dispersed. They all scattered in different directions, like the congregation after church on a Sunday. Only when Saffron and Niger took me back to the rat hidden in the alcove did I realise that it was finally breakfast time, and they were all off in search of something to eat. The three of us made a hearty meal, smacking our lips with enjoyment, although I have to admit that rat meat can't really be described as the most Lucullan of delicacies for our palates. As soon as the worst of my ravenous hunger was satisfied, I found myself longing yet again for Gustav and his almost loving manner of opening tins. Ah, the clatter of the tin-opener! It was like a familiar nursery rhyme to my ears. Oddly enough, poor as their own palates are, humans know how to make food for us better than anyone else. Why they let themselves be fobbed off with terrible fast food and never complain is a mystery to me. At least our feast gave me a chance to widen my culinary horizons. Afterwards my blind employers guided me through a complicated system of tunnels which kept branching in a confusing way. Though I had my eyesight, I was lost in the total darkness of this labyrinth, where not even the faintest ray of light could penetrate. On our way I finally got round to telling the others what had brought me down to the underworld. Of course I assured them, hypocritically, that I had no intention of returning to a life of luxury and tin-openers. The journey finally ended at a drainpipe with bright sunlight falling through it like a vision. Saffron and Niger stopped at this point, looking solemn.

'I don't know if we shall ever meet again, my dear Francis,' said the Lord of the Drains, sounding genuinely sad. His wiry second-in-command, on the other hand, kept her face turned away from me so as not to show her emotions. Maybe she felt a certain melancholy on parting too, but it seemed she wasn't going to forgive me for the defeat of Rhodes in a hurry.

'But sometimes a single meeting can change a person's whole life,' Saffron went on. 'We aren't actually asking you to change. We just want you to remember us when we're out of your sight. Don't forget that these sewers contain not only the effluent of an ever-festering world but also the invisible Company of the Merciful, which gives new life to brothers and sisters condemned to death. You have a hard puzzle to solve out there, and no one can ever repay you. But nothing less than the lives of our own kind in the country depends on your solving the case. Because if Crazy Hugo and that brutal dog go on with their butchery the results will be worse than a plague. We outsiders may seem phantom figures, only half alive, yet life is the holiest thing we know. Life seems the most natural thing in the world to the young, the intact and the carefree, but for those who shake hands with death daily it's a rare exception from the rule. We're fighting for that exception, and I hope you'll fight on our side too, my dear friend.'

As he uttered these solemn words Saffron kept his head tilted to one side, so that the sun falling through the drainpipe shone on his right earring. The glowing, shining gold reflected the light, which dazzled me, transporting me into a state of magical reverie. I couldn't suspect him of doing it on purpose, because he had no way of knowing the exact position of my eyes. On the other hand, down here I wasn't dealing with well-fed old farts lying about in armchairs who'd lost all their instincts. People who were constantly confronting unusual situations in such an inhospitable environment must have unusual methods at their command too. In any case, using suggestive tricks of this kind to bind me to my detective mission showed shrewdness which wasn't to be underestimated.

At last the grimy Goliath bent down to me and gave me the fraternal kiss, rubbing his nose affectionately against mine. For a race of individualists like us, this intimate gesture is the ultimate sign of confidence and trust, rather like – well, let's say rather like one human lending another his credit card.

'I'll do everything I can not to disappoint your blind people, Saffron,' I told him. 'And if a brilliant detective gets washed into this Venice of a sewage system some day minus his head, then you'll know that Hugo and his dog have escaped arrest by underhand means. God protect you!'

I turned away, and was about to scramble up the drainpipe when a paw gently touched my back. I turned back and looked straight into Niger's glowing white eyes. You could tell from her twisted expression that she was forcing herself to whisper a few last conciliating words to me at the moment of farewell. But before she could lose face like that, I took the initiative and rubbed my nose against hers. She returned the caress, and I suddenly thought what victims of circumstance we are. In other surroundings, under other conditions, our meeting would have gone very differently; she and I might even have mated. In another time, Niger, in another world, I said silently to myself, things would have turned out differently . . . And as I was trying to overcome this overwhelming fit of melancholy, I suddenly knew with complete certainty that I would indeed see Niger and Saffron and all the other blind ones again, and very soon at that – but in another time, in another world.

CHAPTER 4

A new life, a second life! To leave the old, threadbare, failed life behind and begin all over again: which of us hasn't dreamed of such a wonderful chance? I was prey to this illusion myself as I scrambled through the drainpipe to freedom. The euphoric sense of a new start was boosted by the fact that the scene into which I emerged was one of unrivalled natural beauty. The opening of the drain was at the foot of a small hillock beside a romantically babbling brook. A fallen ash tree lay across this stream, forming a natural bridge. The brook itself wound like an idling snake through breathtakingly lovely wooded meadows. Last night's storm suddenly seemed just a dismal nightmare, for the rays of the sun shone on the thick carpet of flowers as brightly as if they'd had a thorough overhaul in the interim. The dampness left by the rain had raised gossamer clouds of mist which were doing a veil dance round the budding branches. Myriads of bees and butterflies whirled cheerfully in the air like confetti. Starlings and nightingales sang as if competing for a deal with a recording company.

Rather dazed, I tottered off into this sea of light, chlorophyll and intoxicating fresh air, overcome by a sense of being actually reborn. And no wonder; the past few hours had provided me with as much excitement as I'd had in the whole previous year. On entering this green paradise, moreover,

I seemed to have left behind not only all physical dangers and unedifying tales of murder, but my entire misspent past. I suddenly felt no great urge to go back to Gustav's cosy flat and have my libido mashed into nut spread. On the other hand, I wasn't particularly keen to carry out my promise, go looking for a chronically ravenous mastiff and a member of my own species with the engaging manners of a Nosferatu, read them their rights and then haul them before a justice blind in both eyes. No, my future, my second life would all be like this happy moment: light-hearted, natural, carefree.

A young tree on the opposite side of the stream attracted my attention. Its buds were fully open. The pink, bell-shaped blossom it bore sent out signals proclaiming the sheer joy of life, and its filigree branches swayed in the warm breeze like angels beckoning. Since I'd involuntarily taken an overdose of liquid in the sewage system, I felt an urgent need, as a convert to nature worship, to pay homage to this gem of the wilderness and promote its survival with some biologically degradable fertilizer. So I trotted over the mossy trunk of the ash to the other side of the brook and hurried on over the outer roots of that centuries-old fallen Methuselah of a tree to the spot I'd picked for irrigation. When I finally reached it, my bladder already relaxing nicely in anticipation – the tree blew up.

First I thought it was an optical illusion, then I thought it was a wonder of nature, and finally I thought it was some kind of hocus-pocus staged by Saffron and Niger for the amusement of all and sundry. I saw the central part of the trunk, which was as thick as a human arm, explode into a thousand splinters, whereupon the crown of the tree folded, tipped over and fell to one side, leaving only a jagged stump behind. Extraordinary: the pretty tree was shattered, like a happy dream when the alarm goes off. A fraction of a second later, however, I realised that while I'd seen the wood splinter at close quarters I'd heard the crack of the explosion somewhere off to one side. I began to entertain nasty suspicions. . .

My head swung round, and I inspected the area in alarm. In rapid succession, as if they were snapshots, I registered a series of views of this virgin landscape, which suddenly seemed to be swarming with giant prehistoric ash trees and secret societies of druids. Or was it all just a hallucination, the result of exhaustion and stress? But the tree in front of my nose really *had* blown up: I could swear it. If it hadn't, if I was going to fall for such an impossible phantasmagoria in broad daylight, then my brilliant mind needed urgent attention. Notwithstanding, I feverishly went on looking for some rational explanation – and I finally found it.

The stronghold of the Evil One rose behind a marshy pool at about the right distance. It might blend into the tapestry of speckled light and shade formed by the undergrowth in the background, but normally it would be easy even for someone with only moderate vision to spot it. My failure to notice it immediately was simply due to my overheated nerves, which had been expecting something wholly supernatural. However, what I saw was nothing but a time-honoured classic of deer-stalking methods: a raised hide, officially for watching so-called game, but in actual fact a sneaky place of concealment for people whose hobby is murder. A tall figure stood in this hide, watching me intently through a pair of field-glasses. Sinister shadows surrounded it, and the reflection of the field-glasses sprang out from these shadows like the eyes of a wolf glowing in the night. However, if a fleeting flash of light hadn't caught my attention I'd have overlooked the figure completely. The brief flash came from the barrel of the gun in the watcher's other hand. As far as I could tell from this distance, the gun was really something special. It didn't have a conventional wooden stock, but consisted of a metal curve all in one piece, resembling a sporting rifle only in outline, with the rather bolt-like barrel resting on this stock and gleaming dull silver. You'd need to be a champion shot to take precise aim with such a massive weapon. The alarming guardian of these meadows was rigged out in the North American version of his profession's costume, with a red and black check lumber-jacket and a matching woollen cap with earflaps. At this point he quickly put his field-glasses down in order to resume his mopping-up duties, and as I watched, wide-eyed, he pointed his gun at me again and concentrated on taking aim. As he did so I got a glimpse of the nickel-framed sun-glasses he was wearing; they had mirror lenses. It wasn't likely he could miss me and hit the tree this time; his first failure to hit the target had obviously made him correct his aim. I simply couldn't imagine why he was after me. I didn't look particularly like a rabbit. However, the hunter obviously felt otherwise, and before I had a chance to introduce myself to him as a gentleman of intellect and education, he was blasting away again.

With instinctive presence of mind I took the biggest forward leap of my life, aware at the same time of the final cracking of the tree trunk behind my back. I saw flying splinters of wood whiz past me. Saints above, the bloody lunatic really meant it! The sudden flood of adrenalin into my cells made me act without thought, my mental processes reduced to those of a grasshopper. Everything I did was automatic, unplanned, purely instinctive. Where on earth could I go to escape this fierce salvo of artillery fire? There – *there* was safety! Like a revelation, a hollow tree with a crack in its trunk loomed up ahead of me, offering the ideal refuge, or anyway temporary cover. But the next bullet was already thudding into the ground only a few centimetres from my paws. It made a little crater, forcing me to swerve sharply off in the other direction, like a hare. If the marksman had been entertaining any lingering doubts about his rabbit theory my behaviour would dispose of them once and for all. In the most remote corner of my upper storey my analytical faculties stirred, despite the mortal danger I was in, and I compared human notions of hunting and our own. While my kind has specialised in the unattractive rodent tribe, man destroys everything he can get in the sights of his gun just for the hell of it, without any obvious necessity, and even prefers members of his own species. A very peculiar way to get your fun. Can it really be true, I asked myself, that nature once dropped a stitch and produced a creature whose megalomaniac inclinations will drive it to murder its own ancestral great-great-grandmother, like some incurable psychiatric case? But why? What for? To set itself up as God the Father? How else can we account for the millions and millions of animals pursued, mutilated and massacred by hunters? How else can we explain all the other monstrous things men do? But in that case nature herself is nothing but a botched monstrosity.

My train of thought came to an abrupt end when another bullet knocked a great hole in a low branch as I brushed past it in my headlong flight. Flying splinters struck my head; coarse wood dust got into my eyes and blurred my vision. Now that I was stumbling clumsily about like a clown in grotesquely large shoes, the shooting had stopped. Which could only mean that the marksman was reloading.

I saw the vague outline of a line of bushes some way off. There was a gap in it, and a bright light lured me that way. As I was still wondering whether to try going through this loophole, I heard the next shot. This time the projectile singed a small tuft of fur on my left side, and before I could immerse myself any further in the decision-making process I was sprinting for the bright gap as if someone had stuck a hot needle up my arse. The hunter just kept on firing, but I didn't care about that. The one thought in my mind was to get through the gate to light and safety.

When I finally disappeared into the bushes and came out

again the other side, I found myself taking a crash course in a kind of reality to which I had previously been a stranger. That is, of course I'd seen such idiocies of *Homo sapiens* in literally concrete form, but not personally, only as what I took to be part of a particular horror film which appeared on the small screen with monotonous regularity. As my eyes gradually cleared again, they saw a spanking clean six-lane motorway, and on it a river of metal without any distinct beginning or end, engaged in pointless, compulsive movement. So I'd thought myself in Arcadia only a few minutes ago? Sadly, I had to admit that the Garden of Eden had all the cheery ambience of a rifle range, and if you wanted to escape there were dangerous metal monsters just waiting to flatten any deserter. A trap if ever I saw one.

I got up on my hind legs, leaned on the barrier beside the hard shoulder, and watched the river thundering past for a moment. Obviously the people who built this thing had never for a moment envisaged any kind of living creature but motorists existing in their wonderful landscape. How a person on four legs was to cross this infernal road where vehicles were shooting to and fro the whole time without being turned into pinkish entrails pâté was a mystery, and suggested that the builders had included mass murder in their calculations. I wondered where all those cars were going – or were they on their way back from somewhere? I thought of a stupid human saying: 'There's always something going on wherever we aren't.' Humans seemed to act on that precept, forever chasing happiness like hyper-mobile Sisyphuses and never getting within touching distance, rather as if they were setting out to cross the rainbow.

The next bullet hit the barrier and exploded with a terrifying screech. So the bushes behind me didn't obstruct the marksman's view, as I'd hoped; on the contrary, they were an ideal canvas on which the sun showed me in silhouette. Startled into movement by the shock, I ran into the road without thinking and raced across. I hadn't really expected the monsters roaring by to stop and wave me on in a friendly manner, but I had a vague memory of hearing, more than once, that even the most macho road-hog will step on the brakes, purely as a reflex action, when he sees something unexpected in his way. Lies, all lies! A lorry thundered towards me at full speed, and before I knew it all its hundreds of tons were passing over me like a derailed goods train. Pressed flat as a pancake against the asphalt, I didn't move, only a hair's breadth away from total derangement. When the colossus had thundered on, I tried a frantic sprint for the central reservation of the motorway, but I hadn't anticipated the nippy sports car which was just overtaking the lorry. The sight of this monster on wheels burned itself on my retina just as the sight of the furious bull is burnt on the eye of the incautious torero. It was an amazing machine, red as blood, paintwork gleaming, full of unbridled power and shaped like a steel dinosaur's egg. And as I stood there, rooted to the spot in awe and horror and staring at my executioner, I suddenly knew with total certainty that this masterpiece of engineering was Lucifer in person, bent on annihilating God's creation in the most brutal manner possible. I held my breath, aware that I was about to meet my Maker in order to ask him the reasons for such destructiveness in person.

But God obviously makes exceptions, at least where I'm concerned. Someone or something struck me, and I actually felt the impact going right through my body, flinging me forwards to the edge of the central reservation. Before I could give the red scourge a farewell glance it had disappeared again in search of new victims. I was beginning to feel numb, and I'm not too sure how I managed to cross the other half of the motorway. However, one last record-breaking leap took me over the barrier on the far side.

Even while I was still in the air, a strange sensation that I was moving in slow motion came over me. I felt a bubble of euphoria burst inside me, setting off shudders of thankfulness in spite of my physical aches and pains. I'd cocked a snook at malevolent Fate yet again. Things could only improve from now on. But when I looked down in free flight, so as to coordinate my landing the other side of the barrier, I was sorry to see that it was still going to be uphill work, only uphill work going downhill, as it were, because who'd have guessed that the metal barrier beside the road had a steep slope beyond it, almost a precipice, going at least fifteen metres down? It looked as if it were padded with foliage, but there were numbers of young evergreens waiting for me like a fakir's bed of nails. In a tight corner like this no doubt James Bond would have plucked a parachute from his shoe, but yours truly had to make do with a hoarse yell for help and put his faith, such as it is, in what's said to be the most flexible set of bones and muscles in the world. My euphoria changed to sheer panic while I was still in flight, well before I came down in the vale of woe beneath me.

It wasn't surprising that I landed on all four paws as usual, but on this occasion I had a good deal of trouble in spite of our miraculous natural gift. I couldn't get even the slightest foothold on the ground, which sloped so steeply that it was like a terrifying slide. I turned a somersault the moment I touched the ground and then rolled on down that murderous incline, screeching and uttering delirious prayers. As I went down I collided with several young fir trees, which couldn't be expected to refrain from pushing their sharp needles and branches into my coat, like sloshed medieval soldiers armed with sharp spears making someone run the gauntlet. Ecologists don't tell you a lot about this sort of sadism on Mother Nature's part: such was my last thought before I finally came to rest in a bed of bracken, pricked and stung like an inexpert beekeeper. Not only did I exercise the playing-dead reflex, I decided it was the only proper life-style. Good heavens, did all forest-dwelling creatures have such an exciting time every day of their lives? Compared to these stirring events, my entire existence to date had been nothing but deep sleep. Not for the first time since my rash flight, I wondered whether the Almighty really had to come down quite so heavily on my aversion to certain amputations. Mightn't he let something nice happen to me for a change, even if it was only five minutes' rest . . . ?

He did, and in a more spectacular way than I could have hoped for in my wildest dreams.

Her voice was the bewitching hymn of unfathomable temptation addressed by Venus to her devoted servants. Oh, if only I could express that sweet complaint in words, if only I could convey the electrifying sensations that overcame me as I listened to her beguiling song! I was lying in the soft bed of bracken, all four legs outstretched, like a stuffed replica of myself, whimpering softly on account of my fearsome injuries, when the Eve of my desires raised her yearning voice. From the very first I knew that this particular call could not be made by a member of my own species, and yet there was something familiar linking it to the love-songs of our own queens, an unmistakable similarity of melody and tone. The difference lay in the dark depths of the singer's lament, interrupted now and then by an awesome hiss; it seemed to come from a world full of promise and yet still virgin. There was something mystical and wild about that voice, and something very, very demanding.

Instantly the throbbing pain in my limbs seemed about as important as the flatulence of a worm in Kathmandu. I jumped to my feet and looked hopefully around. However, the jungle of bracken grew above my head and obstructed my view, so I prowled away with the requisite caution in the direction from which I thought the voice was coming. On this side of the motorway the forest was rather different from the moist area on the other side; its varied flora consisted largely of oaks and hornbeams. These trees were stalwart ancients whose branches had been allowed to grow unimpeded over the centuries. The love-call of my phantom diva echoed on and on in this labyrinth, which was relatively dark because of the rampant growth of the trees, and for a moment I thought it was just elves playing a trick of sound on me. Perhaps elves really did live in the forest, as the old wives' tales claim. But then two fronds of bracken parted like the curtains in a theatre, and I saw the most desirable female form ever brought forth by the feline creation.

She lay semi-recumbent on a heap of leaves, like a royal sovereign giving audience, and as chance would have it the trees grew in a ring around the spot, forming a natural pavilion. A single ray of sun penetrated a gap in the leaf canopy that was its roof and fell on my forest queen like a spotlight directed on the star of the show, making her resemble an optical illusion with a bright aura. However, I was brought back to earth by realising that this was my first-ever meeting with a member of the species most closely related to us, the European *Felis silvestris*.[8] We of the domesticated kind speak of them respectfully as the Wild Ones. These forest-dwelling Felidae surely have to bear the heaviest cross of us all, and there are very strange rumours about them. Their extraordinarily secretive life-style, which makes it difficult even for scientists to keep them under observation, accounts for the name of 'grey ghosts' that country folk often give them.

I knew all this about the Wild Ones because I'd studied the scientific literature on the subject in the past. At the time I happened to be going through a depressing mid-life crisis, as they call it, and was feeling rather cut off from my roots, so I embarked on this piece of research in an attempt to find my way back to them. But no book in the world could have shown me the overwhelming magnificence of one of these wild cousins of mine in real life. The basic colour of her soft fur was grey tabby with yellowish lights in it. Her powerful head held a pair of penetrating, light green eyes which registered the slightest movements in her vicinity with the sensitivity of a seismograph. My *belle de jour* was about a quarter again as big as me, with a much larger and bushier tail. At present she was rolling lasciviously on the ground and washing her paws now and then before continuing her siren song. I suspected that it wasn't pure chance I found her in this state of extreme excitement: there was a trace of blood and an almost invisible tuft of brown hair at the corner of her mouth. It looked as if she had been hunting unsuccessfully – her prey had probably managed to get away with a slight injury – and was thus denied the release from stress she longed for. So her fierce hunting instincts had changed to an urgent sexual need. I was faced yet again with the curious interplay of aggression and physical passion among our ranks.

Then she spotted me. Our eye contact was like the collision of two suns careering through space, uniting in a flow of boiling lava. No expression of surprise crossed her face when she saw me, only a satisfied smile as if her trap had finally snapped shut. I could smell her delightful odour some metres off, and the unbounded surge of my instincts made me feel I'd faint dead away. I had to mate with this grey ghost on the spot, even if she gave me a bloody nose for it.

'Welcome, little prince!' she began, narrowing her eyes until they were mere slits with the pupils glinting through them. Then she began rolling very slowly on her own axis on the ground, watching me closely all the while.

'Aren't you afraid all alone in this dark forest, so far from your palace?' she inquired. 'Or are you mingling with the people in the time-honoured way, looking for the prettiest girls in your kingdom? You're in luck! Here's your most loyal subject at your command.'

'Hold on,' I said hesitantly. 'For one thing I'm not a prince, and for another you're no one's subject, my dear! No, you're a Wild One, and the most enchanting Wild One

I've ever seen – though I have to admit you're also the first.'

She smiled, purring, and for a moment it looked as if her irises and pupils would fade out entirely, making way for a turbulent turquoise sea.

'Whereas I'd call *you* about as wild as a dachshund, little prince. If you weren't so sweet, I could fancy teaching you a few wild ways. As it is, why not let nature and nurture unite? My name's Alcina. What's yours?'

'Francis – but my true name is Passion! And believe it or not, Alcina, but the real reason you see me here at all is because I insisted on hanging on to my nu . . . er, to the inextinguishable wildness within me. You've set my wild heart aflame, princess, and may all the fire in it now flow into you . . . '

I was whispering these sweet nothings like an oily Latin lover as my paws, almost without my noticing, stealthily brought me prowling towards her. I didn't know if she realised what my stop-and-go tactics were in aid of, but I was going to considerable trouble to move a bit closer whenever she turned her head away. In a very short time I was right next to my self-styled loyal subject, drinking in all the concentrated force of the impression made on me by the sight and scent of her. The odours emanating from her glands drove me positively mad with desire, and her sinuous movements almost had me flinging myself on her like some clumsy beginner. Only her aggressive spitting, growling and snapping prevented me from losing control entirely and getting my coat decorated with a pattern of painful love-bites. Such behaviour may seem inappropriate to the act of mating, but it's normal in queens on heat, something I have often regretted in view of the positively submissive sexual attitude of the human female. However, Alcina's perilous Black Widow charms drove my desire to incalculable heights quite new to me. What I intended to do, or rather what the urge which had taken possession of me intended to do, entailed considerable danger. I was going to mate for the first time with a beauty not of my own species and whose habits were entirely unknown to me. But carnal lust is like a torpedo: once it's fired you can't bring it back and it won't rest until it has reached its target, even at the price of self-destruction. I might be about to unite with an angel of death, but I braced myself and then, in defiance of my previous experience of love, I made a rush at her.

It was my good luck that I caught her just as she was finishing a roll, so that she'd seen my attack only out of the corner of her eye – and my bad luck that as she was lying on her back she had all four paws free to rake my face into bloody furrows with her sharp claws. I should have known better, dammit! She hadn't even pressed her body flat to the ground, let alone swung her tail over to the side to expose the glowing gateway of passion. Perhaps my rash action didn't come into the category of stupidity after all, but was just the randiness of a dirty old man. Well, anyway, I had to make the best of the situation I'd set up. We went for each other with our claws, but though stabbing pains pierced my body, erotic frenzy brought me to a state of ecstatic anaesthesia in which I relished every stab as the sharp spice to an exquisite meal. Meanwhile I could smell her hot breath as it came out in gasps through her shining incisors. It smelled of burning sulphur, as if her passion would spew fire at the whole world, it smelled of the harsh winds of the savannah – and it smelled of blood. It seemed she'd been able to do more damage than I'd thought to the prey that got away. Locked together like two wrestlers in mortal combat, we were now performing a breakneck dance of dark lusts which showed love in its true aspect: an eternal struggle for release. I tried to grasp the scruff of her neck in my teeth and exert the carrying grip that would make her freeze. However, as her blows and bites grew fiercer, making my body begin to feel as if it were being dissected alive, cold rage came over me. I flung myself on her with a shrill cry, forced her to the ground and sank my teeth into the scruff of her neck – just far enough for her to feel them prick, but of course no further. She immediately gave vent to an imploring whimper, raised her rump in the air, swung her tail over to one side and showed me her precious treasure.

We mated before the eyes of the ancient gods, to the accompaniment of jungle drums and the call of grotesque, curved horns. Those gods, who needed no cathedrals to make themselves heard, blessed us with a sense of total union. We merged with one another wholly, at the same time merging with the forest, the light, the life present in every atom of our surroundings. All her passionate whimpering beneath me, all my groans of bliss, all around us that was cracking, chirping, or even just existing in silence, all this swelled to a river of sound that made our inmost being tremble. The old gods without human features, gods who grew horns and bristles, gods who grunted and squeaked, the true gods of the wilderness urged our bodies on: more, more, faster, faster! At the moment of climax we died, becoming earth, plants, water. Yet at the same time we were reborn many times over through the miracle of impregnation, as creatures superior to all others, with the strongest muscles and tautest sinews, the most exquisite bones and the purest blood. We ourselves became those primeval gods to whom sacred nature really belongs.[9]

When I got off Alcina and scurried for cover, my life-giving tool was just about bursting with its exertions. The tiny sharp spines on it which stimulated ovulation in her paradisal grotto had hurt, so her aggressive tendencies were now like a can of kerosene begging for a burning match. Pleasure and pain, the perfect Siamese twins. I would have another go at her later, and she would let me, but for the moment we had to content ourselves with cleaning our overheated reproductive equipment. I set about this pensive occupation with my sandpaper tongue, but my partner was not quite so particular about cleaning. She mewed frantically, let herself fall sideways on the leaves, and began the game of rhythmic rolling all over again.

'Run out of steam already, little prince?' she gasped, curling her paws sensuously into little hooks. 'At home in your palace I suppose you ring for the court doctor to come and give you a fortifying suppository after such exertions.'

Now that my mind was beginning to clear again, I was struck by the way she expressed herself. Did all members of the *Felis silvestris* species employ this refined style, or was I just a victim of received notions about the rough way country bumpkins are supposed to talk? The various branches of our family have no difficulty in communicating with each other, except for those of our relatives in whom the bone at the root of the tongue is replaced by cartilage. Lions, tigers, jaguars and leopards, including snow leopards and clouded leopards, have a language quite unlike ours, and unlike us they can roar. Of course every species has its own dialect, but I very much doubted whether all the Wild Ones spoke in such high-flown terms. My curiosity stimulated by all the excitement, I decided to ask a few questions.

'Don't worry about supplies, Alcina. There are funds in reserve, and not just in the bank where sturdier males than I are required to give of their best. But it could be we've chosen the wrong spot for genetic experiment. It so happens that just before I met you a hunter's bullets narrowly missed me. I suppose you Wild Ones are used to running such risks.'

'That's the trouble with you townies: you think too much instead of using your instincts, except maybe to study some human's appearance and draw conclusions about the kind of scraps he'll throw out so that you can make a beeline for the edible contents of his dustbin later. You've gone soft! You're beggars and scroungers too! If you were better acquainted with our tribe then you'd know it's more likely we could leave a little pile of shit on a hunter's head unnoticed than that he'd ever get to see one of us.'

'Hey, what happened to your proper respect for your little prince all of a sudden, sweetie? And incidentally, isn't your own verbal style some way from the noble savage? The way my pathetic blunted instincts see it, you lot don't seem to be particularly good hunters yourselves. Unless I'm much mistaken you didn't get anything but a tuft of hair from the game you were chasing just now.'

'Well, fancy that! So our little prince turns out to be a brilliant detective! OK, so maybe that cunning rabbit did slip through my paws. These things happen. But there's more dignity in accepting such failures than in eating carrion from tins.'

'Not if the tins were designed by Philippe Starck, but never mind that for now. Alcina, I want to ask you what may sound a rather peculiar question. I won't go into the circumstances which brought me to this jungle in detail, but I must tell you that I learned some terrible things on the way, during an interlude in the realms of darkness. And I was told that universal harmony hadn't exactly broken out up here in the bosom of nature either. I gathered that brothers and sisters of my kind living on the local farms were in particular danger from terrorists . . . '

'Oh, you must mean the Black Knight and his bloodthirsty goings-on.'

I felt my concentration drain away from my testicles and go back up to my brain. Really, my natural perversity was enough to make a cat laugh: faced with the choice between the amusements proper to my species and intellectual diversion, I always plumped for the latter! Not so long ago I'd been disowning any detective ambitions, with a view to beginning a new, carefree life as a tiger. And here I was already, in the middle of a not very veiled interrogation about something that was really none of my business. Curiosity, that old ruling passion of mine, seemed to have consumed so much of my brain that it was no more use for anything but solving mysteries. So now I was playing Chief Inspector in the Case of the Black Knight, without the faintest idea of the deadly consequences still ahead of me.

I must mean the Black Knight, must I? So that freak of nature was obviously famous in these parts. It was a wonder no animal conservationist had turned him in yet.

'You know him?' I asked.

'Well, we don't precisely swap recipes, if that's what you mean, but every child around here knows that he and his crazy dog are persecuting your farmyard friends.'

'Have you ever seen him commit one of his crimes?'

'No.'

'Has anyone else seen him do it?'

'No idea, but he's certainly at large in these woods. You're bound to come across him yourself some time if you stick around long enough. There isn't a shadow of doubt about that, or the fact that we're always having to save wilting Willies like you who've lost their way from starving to death.'

'Oh yes? I rather thought neither of us had anything to complain about where willies are concerned. But never mind that: I can't help noticing your teeth are not exactly chattering with fright at the thought of the monster.'

'Brilliant observation. We're immune to him, you see.'

'Why?'

'Do you really have to ask? Oh, Francis, the scraps of meat your master offers you as culinary delicacies have obviously clouded your powers of reasoning! Don't you really see any reason why my kind are spared the horror of the Black Knight?'

'Well, just off the cuff . . . '

'It's because we'd tear him to pieces if he touched a hair of our heads. We are the Wild Ones, the only true lords of the forest. We dance to its song when the wind whistles over the tree-tops, we honour the sloughing of its skin when season succeeds season, we preserve and care for it by hunting and thus keeping its surplus population down. We are its eldest children and most faithful guardians, we're so closely merged with its being that we've even taken on its colour. No one in these parts would dare to harm us. If he did, the spirit of the forest would rise against him, along with all the spirits of my tribe.'

'Scroungers like me are a bit slow on the uptake, you know, but even at the risk of seeming more stupid than you and the rest of the Forest Police will allow, I have to ask you one more simple question. If you're so invincible and so fearless, then why don't you dispose of the Black Knight and put an end to the farmyard murders?'

'First, because we feel anything but sympathy for the victims. They're a lazy lot, and they suck up to human beings. They'd rather crawl to the destroyers of our hunting grounds than make an honourable living by hunting for themselves. Of course they do catch the occasional mouse and fool the stupid farmer into believing his investment in milk and scraps is paying off. But actually, out here in the country the stupid rodents will walk straight into your mouth regardless unless you happen to be in an airtight zinc coffin. I'm sure you'd get on splendidly with those layabouts. You could hold story-telling competitions, for instance, about the way-out "sweet" little attitudes you adopt to persuade your owners to throw you their half-eaten delicacies.'

'So what about the second reason? I mean, I really am gradually gathering some vague notion of the meaning of dignity, you know.'

'The second reason why we can't bring ourselves to send the Black Knight packing is directly connected with the first. After all, the Knight and his servant the dog have chosen to live wild and free, utterly despising the crumbs man would throw them in return for acting all cuddly. In that they resemble us.'

'But they're crazy. They're killers!'

'Aren't we all? What do you think your tinned food is made of, my dear Francis? Waste paper? Believe you me, lover boy, the treasured titbits you eat once breathed air, felt the warm sun on their coats and enjoyed life too. The strong eat the weak. Ever heard of that principle before?'

'By that reasoning we ought to worship human beings as gods. They aren't just strong, they're all-powerful.'

'You and your like already do worship them! But the fact is, mankind has a choice, unlike us. And speaking of choice, I obviously made quite the wrong one when I picked you. All this talking has put me right off sex. You strike me as a proper windbag.'

Windbag, wilting Willie, scrounger – and when our liaison began I was her little prince. I was coming to understand how ardent love can turn to the vicious sparring of divorce. That's something which can take humans years, but my kind can do it in a few minutes. As if her strings were being pulled by invisible fingers, Alcina suddenly leaped to her feet and shook herself vigorously. Her passionate rolling had left little clods of dry mud in her fur, and they shot off in all directions as if there'd been an explosion. Once this thorough cosmetic operation was complete she stood before me again in all her radiant beauty, and I was very sorry that I hadn't kept my mouth shut after our tender passage and started right in where we left off. As she attentively licked her delicate parts clean, I was overcome by deep melancholy. I knew she would continue on her lustful way for several days, until her passion ebbed like a swing running down and finally came to a halt. And on that way she would encounter many willing victims, like me, who were more than happy to give the swing another push. I'd wasted the chance of a honeymoon lasting several days and nights, and all because of my inveterate curiosity. I almost wished that hunter would come back and give me the *coup de grâce*. It would just serve me right for my hopeless stupidity.

'Francis, don't mind too much if your loyal subject must go in search of a new prince now,' she said softly, turning away and walking off, her rump swaying gracefully, into a rampant colony of mushrooms. It was like the final chord of a gripping opera in which the entrancing prima donna is swallowed up by theatrical clouds, to become a transfigured tabby cloud dissolving into the firmament herself.

'It may console you to know that our meeting has not been in vain. You've made me think. Perhaps we ought not to take the Black Knight's butchery so lightly after all. I'll discuss it with our leader, my beloved and highly respected mother Aurelia. When she's made her considered judgement, you may put your views to the members of our tribe, and then we'll all decide what to do about it.'

'But how will I find you and your tribe?'

'Never mind that. If you stay around in this forest we'll find you, my little prince!' she said, disappearing among the gigantic fungi. Although I was still struggling to overcome the pain of farewell, part of my reasoning power was occupied with her sudden change of mind. Had a mere mental nudge really been enough to influence her sense of justice? Or were her last words to be taken as nothing but a conciliatory, noncommittal goodbye? No, I couldn't believe that, not of a member of so proud a race, a race which set such store by keeping its word. In the end I had to content myself, feebly enough, with surmising that I'd been really convincing without actually meaning to. This had been an unusual meeting in many ways – and a failure in many ways too.

Five minutes had passed before I began trying to think of a way out of this tricky situation. I'd simply been sitting in the ray of sunlight which pierced the leafy canopy, staring as if entranced at the fungal sea into which she had plunged. I felt as if I could still sniff her lustful scent in the air, see her fluffed-up coat, the colour of smoke, hear her deep voice, like the echo of prophecies from some sibylline goddess. Oh, shit and bloody hell, why did a poor old mental acrobat like me always have to fall for this sort of female? Why couldn't I fancy a fluffy Persian for once, just for a change, a queen with an IQ so low as to be barely measurable? A female who handled the business of love with all the refinement of battery farming, and apart from that went to her food bowl like an addict to the needle? But no, I had to pursue these standoffish ladies whose attitude was: thanks a lot but I have a good brain of my own! And who gave you the feeling you were indispensable only as long as your snorkel was up and working. Afterwards, you could sink to the bottom of the sea again for all they cared. I didn't even dare think what sort of progeny would be born of such relationships. Very likely future generations would meet only at exclusive pedigree shows and swap genes in vacuum-sealed plastic bags.

Despite my changed circumstances, I felt the old biological demands asserting themselves again and alerting me to an urgent need. I'd satisfied my hunger to some extent down in the sewers, and then, against all expectations, I had also satisfied those appetites which mankind for some inexplicable reason likes to describe as animal, although of all existing species *Homo sapiens* carries on with least restraint in that area. Well, as a wilting Willie of urban origin with ears attuned to the clatter of the tin-opener, I hadn't actually cut too bad a figure so far. All I needed to top off my good luck was some sleep. It was now late in the afternoon, so over fifteen hours had passed since I first set out, and in all that time I'd been wide awake and under great stress. All this would be a strain on humans, but one they could cope with; for someone with finely tuned senses like mine, however, long-term stress can soon induce total breakdown. As we are extremely efficient hunters who usually spend a lot of time lying in ambush, we need three-quarters of the day for sleep, unlike the naked ape. And if we have to go without sleep we're bound to collapse.

The sun would soon be setting, and then this lightly wooded jungle would become eerily hostile territory. Who knew, perhaps Crazy Hugo and his canine aide themselves might do me the favour of removing any lingering doubts I had of their guilt, along with my head? I may be classified as a nocturnal animal, but the idea of sleeping unprotected in the dark undergrowth made me exceedingly uncomfortable.

So I forged ahead. I was looking for either a narrow crack between some rocks or a tree that would be difficult for others to climb: anyway, a refuge which might lack the comforts of the Presidential Suite in the Waldorf Astoria but where I could at least lull myself into a belief that I'd hear any intruder coming a long way off. And my hopes of a suitable place were far exceeded when, after I'd walked a little way, the forest suddenly came to an end, giving me a view of a valley. In the middle of this lush green hollow lay a dilapidated property consisting of a romantically shabby farmhouse, two wooden sheds, and a large farmyard. The stream that had first welcomed me ran past one side of this farmyard, and the forest trees began again beyond it, rising up a steep hill, so the property in the valley was like a little bridleway of civilisation running through the woods. The fields which belonged to the farm obviously lay elsewhere, some way off.

The sight of this oasis made me forget all about trees and cracks between rocks; all I wanted, as if in proof that Alcina's rude remarks were right, was to make myself agreeable to the humans here. Surely they wouldn't chase a handsome fellow like me away. In fact it was more than likely that one or two of my kind were already giving the humans of this farm their company, satisfying mankind's need for something to pet in return for scraps of whatever got slaughtered on the farm. In my mind's eye I already saw myself tucking into a steaming heap of fresh offal, splashing in lakes of milk. Even better, I was enormously cheered by realising I wouldn't have to spend the night out in the forest now; I could be a civilised settler, safe inside the blockade, with a notice on the gate saying No One at Home to deter any ill-intentioned savages. Of course there was a risk of some officious farm dog who considered the lonely farm sacred ground and his bucolic owner the Lord God Almighty trying to chase me off. Or there might be unwelcoming members of my own species who'd turn nasty and fan the flames of territorial dispute. But I felt sure that thanks to certain techniques borrowed from the art of surgery, and which I had mastered as well as the chief surgeon himself, I could deal with any such opposition.

So I ran jubilantly downhill. I was pleased to see ponies grazing peacefully in the meadow. The sun was setting in splendour behind the forest on the other side of the valley, and the whole landscape, sheds in the middle and all, was bathed in a magical glow, as if the rare ore of Contentment was mined here.

When I had almost reached the farmyard but was still some distance away, I saw three of my professional colleagues. One of them, a brown and remarkably sturdy specimen, lay stretched out in the middle of the farmyard, which was semi-circular and paved with cobblestones. He had turned to the setting sun, so I could admire only the visual delights of his colossal rump. Evidently he'd dropped off to sleep in the gentle sunset warmth – either that or he was suffering from a terrible attack of indigestion following a lavish lunch, which suggested that one more mouth to feed made no difference in this spot. The second putative mouser, a tabby, offered a most provocative sight to a person in need like me: he was lying on his back on a huge old barrel right beside the farmhouse door, and he too was turned to the sun. He was obviously quite drunk with sleep, his paws up in the air and bent at an angle, a position our young assume when their owners tickle their tummies. His head was tipped back over the edge of the barrel, so it was hidden from me. I could see nothing of the third member of my species but half of his body, coal black and resting in the sphinx position; his front half was concealed behind the shed on the right. The owners of this place, the ideal setting for an ad trying to sell cigarettes with the tar content of a steam locomotive, were obviously still working in their fields, since apart from a defunct conveyor belt for a potato harvester there wasn't an agricultural implement to be seen in the farmyard. This was a good opportunity to try the hospitality of the rural population, though I might have to thump them a bit by way of persuasion.

As my paws touched the well-swept cobblestones I picked up a penetrating odour. However, I couldn't instantly recognise it, as I usually would have done. The weariness seeping through my nervous system was beginning to blunt the keen apparatus of my senses. Speculating in passing on the source of this unpleasant smell, I approached the big grouchy-looking fellow from behind, having decided to dispense with the submissive etiquette we usually employ in approaching others of our kind. Good heavens, they probably used this one on the other side of the scale for weighing pigs! By now the great orange globe of the sun had sunk beneath the horizon, leaving behind it a breathtaking sky which bathed the idyllic rural scene in theatrical red light. I did think it rather odd that our sleepy friends in the yard hadn't registered my invasion of their territory yet: how did they expect to do their job as rodent terminators with such a useless early warning system? Perhaps there was something in Alcina's dismissive comments on idle layabouts. I was only a metre from the first great lump of lard when the acrid stink increased to the power of ten in intensity. Really, he might at least turn round and fling me an insult or so. And that horrible smell – was it farmyard slurry? Or some kind of chemical for blowing cattle up to twice their proper size? Or . . .

It was blood. A great pool of blood, trickling away, drenching swarms of flies and actually drowning some of the greediest. The fat guy lay in his life's blood, or rather what had once been his life's blood, and his fur was soaked with it. You couldn't see this horrible fact from a distance because his coat had absorbed so much blood that there was only a liquid border left, like a moat round a mighty castle. But now I could see that the blood had risen all the way up the fur of his back. He had deep wounds on his back too, wounds from which jets of blood had spurted not so long ago. When I picked my way round his well-nourished corpse to look at his face I was confronted by the next horror. Both his eyes had been scratched out, so that the jelly of the eyeballs was running down to his muzzle, leaving yellowish tracks in his nostrils. I bent to sniff the wounds. As I did so my nose inadvertently touched his head and it came away from his neck like a ripe fruit, fell to the ground, and left the jagged ends of his windpipe and oesophagus grinning at me like a blood sausage with the end bitten off. That valuable item the conk had obviously been just hanging on by one last half-severed sinew. This pulp of flesh was giving off the smell; in retrospect, I'd subconsciously refused to analyse it because further grim discoveries didn't suit my need for sleep one little bit.

Before I could go stark staring mad with the baffling horror of it all, I turned away and threw up the half-digested remains of the sewer rat I'd eaten on the cobblestones. I then shakily removed myself at once from my close rustic encounter of the first kind and staggered over to the fellow on his back on the barrel. Not that I had any illusions about the state I'd find him in, but only because I saw it as my damn duty to examine these horrors with painful precision, so that I could draw some clever conclusions later. Saffron had assessed my character acutely. I and no one else would solve this brutal case – though God knew how.

However, when I reached the barrel there wasn't a lot left to examine. From a distance, I'd already spotted the inconspicuous swarm of flies over the unfortunate victim, and now I saw what I'd feared. The tabby's head wasn't dangling over the side of the barrel; it lay on the ground behind it like some rejected titbit. I no longer felt particularly anxious to jump up and make a close examination of the full extent of the dreadful injuries. What I'd see would be just the same as in the case of the first corpse. Paws reaching to heaven, the poor creature seemed to be telling me that his soul had just got there, and indeed there was only one good thing about his wretched condition: his sufferings were all over now.

Overcome by grief, I began to weep. In a spirit of rebellion, I called down curses on a nature that could engender such unspeakable horror. The new life I'd intended to begin, only a few hours ago, turned out to be the same old festering tissue as usual, only it came painted green this time. And as usual it hadn't taken long for the first boil to burst. Innocence, in whatever form, was merely a fiction cooked up by total imbeciles or inveterate liars, while evil was the precise mathematical formula accounting for all existence. Evil, in short, was Truth. Our blue-green planet was really a black, barbaric star, sick, pitiless and horribly dangerous; we just didn't notice because we let ourselves be taken in by seductively beautiful mirages.

As tears soaked the fur of my face like the blood soaking through the victims' coats, I staggered on, a wounded but still courageous soldier, to look at the final victim of this senseless fury, the one behind the shed on the right. But turning the corner of the shed I saw that horror can be a matter of quantity as well as quality. The unfortunate victim himself wasn't really responsible for this rise in shock value. With his body rent apart by greedy bites, he was only another version of the grisly sights I'd already seen. Even his torn-off head couldn't horrify me, because it was nowhere around. Presumably the murderer had taken it away as a souvenir, to make himself an ashtray or something similar. What made the tough Inspector's throat constrict with dismay was the view down to the stream flowing so gently by. A ghastly trail of corpses of my own kind, maybe a dozen brothers and sisters in all, led down to the water like a devil-worshipper's abandoned artistic composition. Its macabre final note, as you might say, was the head of a fluffy ginger infant lying on the bank, washed by the gentle waves. They had all been slaughtered in the same way, i.e. with frightful mutilations.

I opened my mouth wide to express both grief and hatred; I was going to strike up a bloodcurdling yowl fit to make the entire universe tremble. But then I suddenly felt something in the immediate vicinity, something like a breath from a strange other world. I turned swiftly, just in time to see the vast shadow of some creature passing along the dirty side wall of the farmhouse. A huge, a massive creature, moving on four sturdy feet, its head as large as an elephant's and nodding up and down. Of course the shadow effect magnified size, making the monster seemed mightier than it really was. In theory, therefore, I might have felt reassured next moment if I had seen the original face to face. But before I got that far I saw something else: the monster's forepaw was sticking out from behind the shed, and that small section of the creature was enough to freeze both the blood in my veins and my brain itself. It was a thumping great paw if ever I saw one; it might have been made for killing. Despite the dim light, I could see that its fur was tawny. It had dark spots, and the paw itself was armed with claws the size of crowbars and sharp as knives. Its circumference was that of a strong human arm, and it had the flexibility of a perfect killing machine. It must be a fugitive from a laboratory, or a new evolutionary species which had appeared in order to wipe out my kind by means of mass murder – in my present precarious situation I really couldn't think of any more intelligent explanation.

This seemed the worst moment imaginable for explanations, since I hardly felt anxious to make the acquaintance of the owner of the vast paw. So I retreated hastily behind the wooden wall before the stranger could come into view. Then I crept down the slope and past all the corpses as quietly as possible, swam the stream and raced for the wooded rise on the other side.

When I reached the trees at last, out of breath and in no state to continue my flight at such headlong speed, I finally looked around me. From up here, the farm in the valley looked just as peaceful as it had from the other side before I climbed down. Three dilapidated buildings, a farmyard, a stream winding picturesquely by: a deceptive idyll, but it's easy to be wise after the event. The only difference this time was the absence of the sunset that had bathed the valley in warm and flattering hues. Now the sky was clothed in dark blue, the first stars were twinkling, and there was a picture-book moon. I had no good reason to feel safe; the monster might have picked up my scent and be telling itself as it stalked quietly uphill that it had room for one more mouthful.

I went on, further and further into the forest, which now looked like a labyrinthine crypt. Those mysterious rustling, cracking, fluttering and howling noises the mere idea of which had driven me towards what I supposed to be the safety of human protection now received me like a diabolical symphony. I was a helpless prisoner in this perverse world of sound. I realised that my pace was becoming slower and feebler the whole time. By now I was rather like a drunk who remembers only outside the pub door that he's put back eight vodkas as well as those ten beers. I felt utterly exhausted, deathly tired, and I had no reserves to call on. In short, my fuel tank was empty. My paws stumbled over branches and slipped on the leaves more and more often. My usually keen eyes could only just make out a vague pattern of tangled plants and trees in front of the starry sky and the silent moon. Finally I came upon a rocky cliff that rose sharply and extended so far that I could hardly go around it.

I finally collapsed at its foot, and lay there motionless. I felt indifferent to everything. So let them all send me to a better world: the Black Knight, the monster with the gigantic paw, the hunters with their high-tech rifles. If there was nothing on the other side but the bliss of eternal slumber, that was OK by me. Life was no big deal anyway. I closed my eyes and dropped off to sleep instantly . . .

. . . Until, as if woken by a distant explosion, I opened my eyes again and looked up at the cliff in suspense. The moon had now travelled some way from left to right, so I'd spent a couple of hours in the land of Nod, although my sleep had been dreamless, heavy and unrefreshing. The Black Knight was sitting on his mastiff on top of the cliff, glaring down at me with glowing phosphorescent eyes. He was utterly motionless, and the moonlight made him look like a medieval engraving. All he needed was a spear and shield held erect. So I'd had a dream to poison my first refreshing sleep after all, a dream of the worst kind. Any moment now the ghostly horror would climb down and tear my head off. Oh, what a lovely dream – and so unpredictable too. But Crazy Hugo and his equally crazy dog didn't come down the cliff. They just stood there like an equestrian statue, utterly motionless, staring. Their shaggy fur, matted by rain and storm, blew in the wind, and there was something derelict about their attitude, as if committing all those murders had made them outcasts, condemned to wander in the wilderness for ever and a day. I'd never seen anything like it before. The worst part was the rider's magically glowing eyes. Because they weren't clouded by the pestilential breath of this lonely demon, but by something more like crankiness, eccentricity, as if they were the eyes of a comical owl.

As I was simply dreaming these things, however, I didn't need to waste thought on such inconsistencies. My eyes closed again, and I lulled myself back to sleep by reminding myself that it was all self-deception, as mentioned above. I also derived comfort from the words of my beloved Schopenhauer, who said: 'The world is a place of punishment, very like a prison, and one of the evils of a prison is the company you encounter there.' So there was really no call to feel surprise!

CHAPTER 5

When I woke up, the Black Knight had dissolved into thin air, thus providing insubstantial corroboration of my dream theory. It was still the middle of the night, though, and the cliff lay there before my paws like a stranded whale. A physical check on myself confirmed that I hadn't been either hugged to death by a monster or turned into a perforated bedside rug by a hunter while I slept. Thank God for that! I felt refreshed and capable of clear thought again, at least to some extent. But along with my mental powers, my awareness of the forest's eerie background noises also returned, and so, consequently, did my fear. Here in the pitch dark, it was like the shadow of a bat spreading its wings very slowly. The horrors I'd seen at dusk the previous evening involuntarily forced themselves on my mind's eye. That empty farmyard, the decapitated, mutilated bodies of my brothers and sisters, the trail of corpses leading down to the stream – the murderous paw! No, I mustn't let these dreadful memories surface, not now. Most of all, I mustn't waste time in lengthy analysis of what had happened. OK, so my kind have no natural enemies, but I couldn't be absolutely sure that a bear strolling by with a rumbling stomach would have passed its A Level in zoology. So I decided on making a determined exploration of this twilight maze, hoping I'd eventually find my way to the Promised Land of tinned food accurately stamped with the sell-by date. Amen!

An owl hooted a mocking accompaniment to my clumsy attempts at rock-climbing, very likely because, from its high vantage point, it could see that the Black Knight hadn't gone away after all, but was waiting eagerly for me on the other side of the cliff with a napkin tucked into his neck. When I reached the top, however, breathless and panting, I was confronted by a surprise of an entirely different nature. Behind the army of spruce trees I saw the windows of a gingerbread house bathed in silvery moonlight. They shone enticingly. The house was on two storeys, built in the style of a log cabin. The owner might well have done some of the building himself; no construction outfit would have lavished such loving care on the romantic details. But what eccentric recluse could be living in the middle of the forest, so far from all mod cons?

Although my yearning for the peace and quiet of human company was temporarily in abeyance, I just couldn't bring myself to steer completely clear of this Hansel and Gretel house. Curiosity raised its head again, as so often when I was about to get into trouble. Half skidding, half galloping, I hurried down from the cliff, firmly intending to do no more than take a quick look at the house from outside. At first I'd seen only outlines and shifting shadows; these shapes began to take on more distinct form. Whereas all I'd registered from the top of the cliff was the fairy-tale look of the place, some odd details now emerged. The first thing I saw on the forecourt of the house – an area of trodden earth from which the trees had been cleared – was a satellite dish. This dish had the diameter of a pub umbrella and was anchored to a metal socket sunk into the ground. Strangely enough, it was painted in camouflage colours, like a military vehicle. Plain lettering on the dish said: ARK. I saw a paddock behind it containing about ten sheep, recently shorn, their fleeces just beginning to grow again. As if to complete the idyllic picture there was one black sheep among them. I felt there was an element of *déjà vu* about this sheep's proud bearing, but I couldn't quite place it. At the same time I heard the now familiar babbling of the brook close by. It seemed to be accompanying me everywhere, like a rubbernecking native watching me.

As I was so close to the house now, of course I felt I had to venture a glance through the windows. Just in time, however, I noticed a treacherous detail: there were two large halogen floodlights mounted on the veranda roof and linked to metal boxes with glowing red diodes. They were monitors to detect movement, no doubt about it: if anyone approached they would bathe the intruder in floods of bright light. Rather an expensive security system for a cottage in the forest. I had no alternative but to skirt the house at a suitable distance until I found a gap in the movement detectors' range. That was easier said than done, because I found that the battery of monitors formed an almost complete circle. It looked impossible to get in without setting off the alarm. The only place not overlooked by these inconspicuous spies was an angular projection where the back of the building met the left-hand long side. The imaginary corridor to the house at this point was extremely narrow, but if I was careful to move in a perfectly straight line there might be a chance of fooling the system.

Feeling as if I was walking through a minefield, I pussyfooted my way down the fictitious path until I was under the eaves, without setting any sirens off or seeing the floodlights turn the place into a set for a movie about the world's most impregnable maximum security jail. Relieved and still rather weak at the knees, I took a quick glance at my immediate surroundings. The neat, tidy look of the front of the house was not kept up at the back. There was any amount of old junk assembled under the eaves – or perhaps it was stuff that someone didn't quite like to throw away. Towers of file binders, indefinable electronic odds and ends, and in particular plastic tubs for medicinal preparations were all stacked there like bankrupt stock. My knowledge of pharmacology was limited, but I thought that a hurried sideways look at the printed directions suggested these tubs had contained medicaments to treat some kind of epidemic. However, much of the rubbish consisted of various utensils and other items which didn't fit into the picture of a business that had folded. There were flattened tubes of paint, frames containing ragged, half-painted canvases, and paintbrushes hopelessly gummed up, all suggesting that whoever lived here wasn't an entrepreneur gone bust but a creative artist seeking inspiration in nature.

All these impressions, which somehow refused to harmonise into a whole, heightened my curiosity, and against my better judgement I decided on a detailed investigation. Still keeping close to the wall, I moved round to the front of the house and then clambered silently up to the wooden veranda. Once there, I got up on my hind legs and pulled myself up to the window-sill next to the front door by my forepaws.

The scene I saw through the open window was far from sensational, but like my first impressions it didn't seem quite consistent with itself. A very thin woman, almost six feet tall, was working frantically away at a huge landscape painting on an easel. Unfortunately I could only see her from behind. She was wearing a black cape like a caftan, and her greying, wavy, carefully combed hair streamed down her back to her hips. Now and then she nervously snatched up her cigarette – not a filter-tipped brand – from the overflowing ashtray standing on a small table and dragged on it with desperate intensity.

Two things, however, pointed up that sense of inconsistency I mentioned. The wall behind the easel was occupied by an enormous set of shelves, every last centimetre of them holding carefully numbered video cassettes. However, the small television set in the room, which itself was only dimly lit by an old-fashioned reading lamp, wasn't at all what you'd expect a video freak to use, although it stood on top of a video recorder which looked particularly luxurious by comparison. All this concentrated audiovisual equipment was like a foreign body in a room which otherwise featured the gear of an artist with a Spartan lifestyle. The other oddity was the picture on the easel. This painting, a woodland scene, had been daubed on the canvas without the faintest spark of talent. It was absolutely terrible. Pairs of eyes glowed between gloomy trees; the artist's models seemed to have been feline orbs. They stared out at the real world almost demonically, like the sick products of a paranoid imagination. Not a trace of artistic quality, but obviously that didn't bother the painter. Dragging on her cigarette as if under some dreadful compulsion, working manically away, she sloshed colours – most of them sombre in hue – on the threatening forest scene she'd already painted as if to drive some kind of evil spirits out of it. You couldn't help seeing that this was some kind of self-therapy.

My spying activities, which were getting to be rather tedious, were suddenly interrupted when my claws inadvertently scratched the wood of the window-sill and gave me away. The painter's head shot round towards me with the lightning speed of a lizard. The face I saw for the fraction of a second scared the living daylights out of me. It was ageless, yet like an old woman's. It reminded me of the faces of children suffering from that mysterious ailment the Methuselah syndrome. Although she was probably in her late forties there was a childlike curiosity in her eyes, yet that curiosity went hand in hand with a vague fear. However, any gleam in those eyes seemed to have been extinguished, and the woman's features were frozen like the face of an ice queen.

Belonging as I do to a species which has made a fine art of developing the niceties of invisibility, I slipped soundlessly down from the window-sill and got underneath it. I heard footsteps above me. They had to mean that the woman was now hurrying over to the window to find out what had caused the sound. After an anxious interval the steps retreated again; obviously her glance outside had borne no fruit.

Of course I could have turned my back on this odd house and its even odder inhabitant at this point and gone on my way. But I was still tempted by the other dimly lit window, up on the first floor. Who knew, I might meet some delightful human there who skinned my kind alive and then roasted their tender flesh over a romantic camp fire while playing *For We Will A-Hunting Go* on the mouth organ. I couldn't let a chance like that slip, now could I? I spotted a tree growing near the veranda; its largest branch bent down towards the eaves of the roof. It didn't look difficult to climb the tree, do a balancing act well within my powers along the branch to the slope of the roof, and then nip in through the window.

No sooner said than done. Once I was up on the tiles after a ridiculously easy manoeuvre, my paws led me straight to the open window, which showed a softly flickering light. Having reached it, I cautiously put my nose into the room. I'd already noticed that this was an odd house, but by comparison with what my astonished glance now beheld, everything I'd seen so far was the flattest normality. To be honest, at first I doubted my own reason, because the sight that met my eyes strongly reminded me of humorous depictions of my species. Believe it or not, but in this room, which was lit by several candles burning in antique branched candlesticks, magic and fairy-tale had really come true, along with a touch of the facetiousness human beings like to project into my kind.

Another member of my species was seated at a solid desk in the old English style. He was obviously male, and of the Somali breed. He was sitting up on his hindquarters in the middle of a chaotic arrangement of open books, untidy papers and inkwells whose contents had been sprinkled all over the desk in large blots. As a long-haired variant of the Abyssinian breed, he had fur of a lustrous apricot colour, thick and slightly shaggy without being at all woolly in appearance. Rather oddly, there was a fine film of moisture on his coat, as if he'd just taken it out of the washing-machine, and a damp patch had also formed around the spot where he was sitting. Although he came of very good pedigree, as you could see from his bushy tail and full ruff, there was something scholarly about his appearance, or perhaps I should say something of the dotty professor. Apart from the shelves lining the walls, full of very old-looking books, he was surrounded by various peculiar objects: wooden totems and primitive masks representing animal gods from Africa, Australian spear throwers and other exotic hunting gear, even genuine shrunken heads. The place felt like an ethnologist's lumber room.

However, what really rocked me back on my heels wasn't this old colonial junk, reminiscent of vanished worlds in the muted candlelight. No, it was the sight of the Somali himself that made my jaw drop in amazement. In spite of his wild origins he appeared to be a confirmed ink-slinger in the most literal sense of the term. What do I mean? Well, it was fascinating to watch! With all the skill of a poet of the Romantic era, he dipped the middle claw of his right paw in the inkwell and then used it to scribble on the sheets of paper in front of him. The velvety fur of his paw acted as a blotter to sop up the ink, and I assumed that he'd sharpened the claw to give it a fibrous texture so that he could use it like a quill pen. Every now and then the writer stopped to think, raised his writing paw in imitation of a great mind meditating, until the Muse seemed to descend again, whereupon he nodded and eagerly resumed work. What on earth was he writing? His memoirs? His doctoral thesis? Or the definitive book on our species and its ways?

My head was whirling, and I felt positively dizzy as I stared open-mouthed at this king of wise guys. But His Majesty was good for yet another surprise. Although I'd taken a lot of trouble to exercise the utmost caution as I prowled around in secret-agent mode, it soon transpired that he could outdo me in even the most primitive matters of instinct. As if his skull had a built-in monitor of its own, he suddenly started, turned swiftly in my direction, and I found him staring right into my astonished face.

We screeched at one and the same time. Don't ask me why, but both the Somali and yours truly were so alarmed by our abrupt eye contact that caterwauling seemed the only thing to do. However, the ink-slinger was clearly in the grip of some much worse anxiety, something which made his whole body vibrate as if caught in an earthquake.

'Please do-do-don't kill me, brother! It was only a jo-jo-joke!' he begged after he'd stopped yowling. As he spoke he put both forepaws up in the air as if I were holding a pistol to his nose.

'Then don't you write anything about my reactions just now, brother! It wouldn't look good in my biography,' I begged him in return.

'Y-y-you mean you won't punish me?'

His face, its apricot glow distorted with alarm, began to brighten and took on the expression of a crotchety old owl again.

'Of course not. Good heavens, they let even the most avant-garde writers live these days! I'm a law-abiding character.'

He frowned, as if baffled. 'Some th-th-things should be explained, stranger.'

I suspected that his stammer was not because of the shock of our meeting. Even at the risk of disturbing him yet more, I took a step into the room. The alarm system outside was making me a trifle nervous.

'Why would I want to hurt a relative? Anyway, I only ever kill on special occasions.'

He calmed down again, put his paws back on the desk and smiled broadly.

'I ge-ge-get the idea. Obviously all just a mis-mis-misunderstanding! My name is Ambrosius. I'm a seeker after knowledge in the field of ESP.'

Hang on a moment! A certain Alcina had introduced me to the bitter-sweet pangs of jungle fever. She had told me that her mother was called Aurelia, and now I met Ambrosius. What was all this – some kind of medieval Scrabble? Well, why not? After all, there seemed to be Black Knights lurking outside. I wouldn't have been surprised if that autumn crocus of a woman downstairs had suddenly come flying into the room on a broomstick.

'Well, pleased to meet you. My name's Francis, and I'm a seeker after knowledge in the field of CTF.'

'CTF?'

'Commercial Tinned Food.'

'I s-s-see. Come on in, Francis. I th-th-think I can help you there.'

Stepping back, he pointed to a corner of the room with his paw. I jumped from the window-sill to the desk and looked that way. The beautiful sight took my breath away. I saw a plastic bowl the size of a swimming pool containing a Mount Everest of chopped meat. There was also plenty of dried food and a bowl of water. It all went to prove no less than the existence of God. I put up a silent and joyful 'Halleluia!' and then, casting good manners aside, I fell upon the spread even before Ambrosius could invite me to tuck in. Only as I sank my teeth into these delicacies did I realise how close I'd been to perishing of hunger and thirst. The stressful activities of flight and mating had drained my body of strength, and my short sleep hadn't made up the deficiency. What I felt during that orgiastic banquet could be described in a single word, a word not much used these days: gratitude. I felt the deepest gratitude to the friend who had seen my need and was instantly ready to share what he had. Indeed, I loved this stammerer. The title of Your Oddity might seem too conventional for him, but he possessed an organ found in fewer and fewer of our contemporaries today: a heart. The only trouble was, I had my mouth too full to express this fervent gratitude.

When at last the bowls were empty, because I hadn't left even a scrap for Mr Manners, and I had delivered my culinary verdict in the form of a satisfied belch that seemed to go on for ever, I got it out. 'Thanks, Ambrosius! You saved my life. And that's not just a manner of speaking, friend.'

'It t-t-takes a bi-bi-bit more than that to save a life, Francis. Glad you enjoyed it. I li-li-live in luxury myself. My companion Diana ha-ha-has gone a bit funny in the head since burying herself in this forest. But the le-le-less normal she got, the more care she lavished on her little da-da-darling.'

It was on the tip of my tongue to remark that her little darling didn't exactly seem to represent the normal EG reading of mental health either, but I managed to swallow my words at the last moment.

'Listen, Ambrosius, I've already seen some odd things about here, even apart from your own amazing skills. For instance, I never heard of a great painter obsessively hoarding thousands of video cassettes before. I suppose she even watches the stupid things too.'

I jumped up on the desk again and took a quick squinny at the handwritten – sorry, paw-written – effusions of my generous host. The contents of those scattered sheets of paper might contain the meaning of life, the universe and everything, but calligraphy was not their author's strong point. They looked more like coded secret messages from the likes of Dr Mabuse. The writing itself was very thin, in accordance with the nature of the writing implement, but the author also seemed to have developed a preference for an ant-like, miniature script such as particularly unsympathetic human eggheads use. Arrows linked the separate entries, as if they were all in some kind of sequence. However, before I could examine the manuscripts more closely Ambrosius lay down sideways on them, obstructing my view, and began calmly licking the ink off his claw. Perhaps he was addicted to the stuff. I couldn't be sure if he had suddenly settled into this comfortable position spontaneously, or if he just wanted to keep me from poking my snotty nose into what was none of my business.

'Ah, I see, you've been doing some sp-sp-spying, my dear Francis,' said my ink-addict friend, with a cryptic smile. Since his mouth was now stained black, he looked like a small child who's been eating too much chocolate.

'However, your conclusions are both right and wr-wr-wrong. Right be-be-because Diana is anything but a great artist, and wrong because none of the videos has a movie on it. They contain nothing but sci-sci-scientific data – or rather stills, pictures showing no movement at fi-fi-first glance. They'd be very bo-bo-boring to a layman, I'm afraid.'

Light suddenly dawned. Why hadn't I guessed before?

'They're satellite pictures! And as the satellite dish out there says ARK on it, I suppose the satellite of that name is picking up information about natural phenomena down here.'

Ambrosius appreciatively raised the greying tufts of hair over his penetrating amber eyes. My swift deductions brought an expression of great surprise to his features, which were very mobile anyway.

'M-m-my compliments, friend! Logic certainly seems to be your strong point. I hope it will be co-co-compatible with mine! But we can discuss that later. Anyway, ye-ye-yes, you're right. Until eighteen months ago, Diana was a scientist doing re-re-research into forestry. With a hi-hi-highly motivated group of young colleagues, she was studying the damage to trees caused mainly by air pol-pol-pollution. On the sur-sur-surface, everything may seem to be g-g-green and lush, but the forest is sick, Francis. In fact it's reached the in-in-intensive care stage without anyone noticing. Wherever he goes, man makes it either a d-d-desert or a rubbish tip. Everything he touched withers in his gr-gr-grasp, everything he looks at burns before his eyes. But then, as if he had a spl-spl-split personality, he struggles fanatically to put things right. Diana's that sort of human. Using expensive fi-fi-filter techniques, the Ark was sending back pictures of wooded areas in various phases of si-si-sickness, shaded in different colours. But then the government suddenly dis-dis-discontinued the research grant, the project was abandoned, the group dispersed. Diana n-n-never got over the disappointment. Ever since she's been guarding the abandoned research station like an embittered mo-mo-mother watching over her child's grave, going more pe-pe-peculiar every day. She's t-t-turned into a real witch in this lonely place. She took to p-p-painting recently to calm her nerves. Even I bl-bl-blush with shame at the results.'

'That's a very sad story, Ambrosius, and I can assure you my own won't have you rolling in the aisles either.'

'I'm sure it's ve-ve-very interesting, though. What sad circumstances can have brought a gentleman like you to this wi-wi-wilderness? Te-te-tell me, my dear fellow!'

So I told him. About Francesca Scissorhands, the terrible storm, the Atlantis of the sewers and its zombie inhabitants, the hunter with the high-tech rifle, the keen motor-racing fans and how I managed to escape them in the nick of time, my wild fling with Alcina, the massacre in the farmyard and my sighting of Monster Paw, and finally my dream featuring the Black Knight in the leading role. As he listened attentively to my story, Ambrosius licked and sucked the remaining ink from his paw and the corners of his mouth. Amazingly, not a single blot remained to mar his looks by the time he'd finished.

'Ta-ta-talk about adventures! Sinbad the Sailor's were a ho-ho-holiday cruise by comparison! Francis, you're a hero,' said the Somali, flattering me quite unnecessarily. 'However, you're wrong about that la-la-last point, my friend. You di-di-didn't dream the Black Knight and his mount, oh no, you saw them all right. They're r-r-real enough.'

'Oh yes?' Something in me was still reluctant to accept the couple's existence. I felt as if I were chasing an imaginary bogeyman.

'N-n-no doubt about it. Saffron, Niger and your wi-wi-wild friend told you so too.'

'However, I've had at least one other suspect since I saw Monster Paw at the scene of the crime in the farmyard.'

'Perhaps you didn't really see that p-p-paw at all. Perhaps you were so horrified you just imagined it.'

'Maybe. But it seemed more real than the Black Knight even when he appeared to me life-size.'

'I d-d-don't understand.'

'Nor do I. But if you put certain coincidences together they come to look like more like Chance's cunning brother, whose name is Delusion. Let me put three particularly notable points to you. First, Hugo and the dog appear to me just when I'm so befuddled with sleep I might take my own reflection for Elvis Presley. Second, the pair of them assume a suitably theatrical position high on the cliff-top as if on a pedestal, so I certainly get an awe-inspiring view of them, but I can't make out a clear picture. They're just shadowy outlines, which heightens the eerie effect no end. Third, our two desperadoes obviously have nothing to do all day but traipse about from farm to farm and try out their teeth on innocent necks to see if said teeth deserve the Consumers' Association accolade of Best Buy. However, the moment they spot a helpless bundle of fur at dead of night, right in the middle of the jungle where they needn't expect any unwelcome eye-witnesses or the arrival of the RSPCA cavalry, they suddenly discover their finer feelings and turn away in remorse. Wouldn't you call that suspiciously touching behaviour for a pair of serial murderers?'

Ambrosius jumped to his feet, swept aside the papers under him with his forepaws so as to get at a blank sheet, and reached for the inkwell again. Then he raised his dripping claw in the air, as if he'd just had another flash of inspiration. His amber eyes were glowing, and his face wore that expression of passionate determination characteristic of zealots with a messianic mission – but also of the deranged.

'Logic!' he cried, as if I had flung some coarse insult at him. 'Logic is your str-str-strong point, Francis! So the way you see it, it mu-mu-must be possible to account for everything in the world by pure reason. But I'm s-s-sorry to say, my dear fellow, the world c-c-couldn't care less about logic. Ask human beings. They can tell you how all their pr-pr-principles and ideals have failed. Logic, Francis, is for logicians in ivory towers trying to de-de-decipher the mathematics of life. In vain, as we know. No, no, no, my fr-fr-friend, chaos rules the world, chaos and madness. And the Bl-Bl-Black Knight and his murderous dog know all about madness. You mu-mu-mustn't think we country folk would cl-cl-close our eyes to these unspeakable murders. But such br-br-brutality rules out any suspects but Crazy Hugo and his mastiff.'

'Why?'

'Be-be-because it's just pointless violence. There are no co-co-conceivable reasons for the crimes.'

'Maybe not at first glance. But take the method of killing, for instance. The murderer or murderers tore the victims to pieces, more or less beheading most of them. Now I ask myself, why wouldn't a clean neck-bite do the trick? Perhaps the victims had something the murderer or murderers badly needed.'

Ambrosius smiled knowingly. 'You mean blood? Or a liver?'

'Well, yes, for the sake of argument. Blood does contain concentrated glucose, i.e. sugar, and proteins. Beasts of prey crave those substances. And the liver contains more sugar than any other part of the body.'

'Well done. The logician in his element. Bu-bu-but tell me one thing. Why doesn't this evil b-b-beast of prey go after his usual game? Its blood contains the same de-de-desirable substances.'

'Ah, now you're turning my own weapons against me, Ambrosius. Of course I can't explain that. I'm just throwing out a net of ideas, hoping the right fish will get caught in it.'

'Very well, my dear fe-fe-fellow, then let's try the me-me-methods of logical detection. First, there's the Company of the Merciful . . . '

He scribbled the words down on the paper with his nimble claw and drew a line all round them. Then he added a question mark. His tiny handwriting made the composition look like something a fly with diarrhoea left behind.

'Who's to say these imitation mo-mo-moles don't leave their gigantic la-la-lavatory now and then and get blood transfusions from their country cousins? From what you say, they d-d-don't object to the odd execution and they have a liking for p-p-painful rituals.'

'That's just what rules them out as suspects, Ambrosius. The pain which has become so much a part of their life would be more than they could bear if they left their bunker. And even apart from the physical superiority of their intended victims, they have no obvious motive. Furthermore, they'd hardly have asked me to solve the case, they'd have done me in on the spot.'

'Right, so let's go straight on to the next suspect, your friend Mo-Mo-Monster Paw!'

He scribbled the name down again, drew another line round it and added a question mark.

'Obviously this creature is a b-b-beast of prey. We've all heard st-st-stories of wild animals seeking out human habitations, lured by comfortable living co-co-conditions there or unguarded farm livestock. In Ca-Ca-Canada, g-g-grizzly bears are said to have overcome their timidity enough to walk into houses in broad daylight and raid the fridge. And in A-A-Africa, elephants raid b-b-breweries because they like to t-t-tie one on now and then. It's a fact. Well, why not? So Mo-Mo-Monster Paw just happens to have specialised in our kind. I expect we really do taste as fabulous as the Chi-Chi-Chinese say.'

'Objection, Ambrosius! If Monster Paw really thinks we taste so good, then why doesn't he eat the entire corpses, skin, fur and all, instead of just a few bites? And why does he go to the trouble of concealing his dreadful deeds, dragging the victims down to the sewers whenever possible?'

'So that just l-l-leaves Hugo and the mastiff.'

Once again he wrote the words down, circled them and added a question mark.

'Hold on! You've forgotten one whole group of suspects.'

'Wh-wh-what group?'

'The Wild Ones!'

Ambrosius roared with laughter, bringing his writing claw down on the paper so hard that his extreme merriment not only produced a well-marked paw print but made drops of ink fly all over the place. Without wishing to sound obsessive about cleanliness, I may remark in passing that my face now looked rather as if someone had been trying out his paint spray on it.

'S-s-sorry, Francis, but that's the si-si-silliest thing I ever heard . . . '

'Before you die laughing, Ambrosius, one simple question: has a Wild One ever featured among the murder victims?'

'No.'

'Isn't it extremely odd that the Black Knight apparently makes a hobby of trying to wipe out our pointy-eared race, but turns a blind eye to the Wild Ones?'

At once my new friend the pen-pusher sobered up again, as if I'd shocked him by breaking some taboo. There it was again: the fanatical gleam in his eyes, the faraway expression that suggested he was drifting away into mysterious dimensions, the unutterable contempt for anyone who cast doubt on the integrity of those sanctified forest-dwellers. I was acquainted with that contempt already, from the élitist wrinkling of Alcina's nose. Ambrosius leaned towards me with the stern expression of a head teacher, and our noses almost touched.

'I'm so-so-sorry, Francis, but now you're talking like a f-f-fool! However, as I know you aren't a fool, you're just trying to pr-pr-provoke me, I'll pretend I didn't hear that last remark. L-l-let me tell you one or two things about *Felis silvestris*. You know, my friend, there's one si-si-sin worse than any other, and that's to slander the victims of a crime by making out after the event that they p-p-perpetrated it themselves. The Almighty has left only a few ma-ma-manifestations of his greatness and goodness here on earth, even f-f-fewer specimens of the wild race, and those are de-de-decreasing every day. I'm sorry to find that you nurture the same pr-pr-prejudice against our wild cousins as humans have felt for th-th-thousands of years. "Incomparable cruelty"- "boundless fury" – those are the kindest things the lords of cr-cr-creation have ever found to say about the Wild Ones. Of c-c-course forestry management reform sped up the pr-pr-process of wiping them out; after the middle of the eighteenth century those reforms tried to turn the forests of the time, which were m-m-more like pri-pri-primeval jungles, into strictly delimited areas of mo-mo-monoculture. It wasn't difficult to wipe out any k-k-kind of animal you liked in such areas. When Paradise dies, Francis, so do the elves, and G-G-God with them. It's a-a-amazing how we ourselves have been infected with human parrot-cries about "exterminating vermin", which entirely fail to understand the true workings of na-na-nature. Resist such wicked fancies, Francis! The Wild Ones are vi-vi-victims, not murderers. If a Wild One were to attack any living cr-cr-creature other than his proper prey, his tribe would tear him apart! The m-m-mere idea is crazy. No, Francis, the Wild Ones *are* the forest, and the forest gi-gi-gives them enough food. The only question is, for how much longer?'

He seemed to have tears in his eyes, so moved was he by his own oratory.

'They're go-go-going to set off for Scandinavia very soon,' he went on. 'There's more prey in the forests there, and be-be-better nature conservation. Aurelia, the leader of the tribe, pl-pl-plans to set off this summer. I'm d-d-doing what I can to help them by looking at the old sa-sa-satellite pictures and picking good routes. In s-s-secret, of course, while Diana's out on her long walks. I meet Aurelia in secret too and pass on the re-re-results of my research. I just hope they make it and find better living co-co-conditions there in the north.'

'You've got me quite wrong, Ambrosius,' I said, rather subdued by this moral battering. Of course I'd suggested the Wild Ones as suspects only as a hypothesis, although Alcina's hostility to her domesticated cousins, and the disconcerting understanding she showed for the Black Knight's dreadful deeds, did give me food for thought. 'You can spare us both any clichés about townies who see creatures of the wild as either dolts or dangerous monsters but haven't a clue about the ecological disaster going on here. I've been deeply concerned about the sad fate of the Wild Ones myself, although in a theoretical way. It's only because we're busy examining a theory for weak spots that I had to mention this dubious point, so do be fair!'

'O-O-OK, I'll take you at your word and he-he-help you.'

He put the Wild Ones down on his list too, but this time, to my surprise, he drew a circle round all the groups named on the paper.

'Although you're an excellent th-th-theoretician, or perhaps *because* you are, of course you haven't thought of the simplest so-so-solution of all. Perhaps the m-m-murders aren't being committed by a single group but by *all* of them!'

I frowned. What was that supposed to mean? 'I don't really get you.'

'S-s-sorry, I put it mystifyingly on purpose. What I mean is, if you don't fancy ma-ma-making the Black Knight your prime suspect, why suspect only those you've already met? There are pl-pl-plenty of other creatures in the forest who m-m-might have committed such crimes. Be-be-because of course we do have natural enemies, whatever people say. For instance the stoat or ermine, thought of by human females only as a soft luxury fur. Stoats are generally believed to attack our li-li-litters; the mother sometimes has to leave them alone in the n-n-nest. They say no litter would survive long in forest areas where there are m-m-many stoats. And they like to eat our livers and suck our bl-bl-blood. Our brothers and s-s-sisters on the farms aren't great on taking precautions any more, so it's easy to imagine a st-st-stoat commando getting at them.

'B-b-but that's not the only possibility. We all know the golden eagle will attack our kind, particularly when the su-su-supply of rabbits and rodents is low as a result of so-so-so-called civilisation. Bones and remains of the Wi-Wi-Wild Ones are found more and more often in the eyries of the lords of the air, but eight times as many remains of our d-d-domesticated kind are found. The list of possible ki-ki-killers goes on indefinitely. Just off the cuff, I can think of hounds gone off their h-h-heads, or lone foxes – they still roam the forest. So I make you a pro-pro-proposition, Francis: we s-s-sleep till sunrise and then set out to make professional inquiries together. We can visit those fo-fo-forest-dwellers who are well-disposed to us – ask them what they th-th-think about the case and if they've ever witnessed any of the crimes.'

'Sounds like a good idea, Ambrosius, but with the best will in the world I can't see how it could work. I don't speak Elkish or Grouse.'

'I do, though.'

'I beg your pardon?'

'You heard m-m-me. I'll interpret for you. Don't g-g-gawp at me like that, Francis! Do you think an old forest gnome like me would have been ki-ki-kicking his heels in this wilderness so long without learning the language of the other gn-gn-gnomes?'

He opened his mouth wide and let out a shrill croak. I couldn't say for sure whether the demonstration was meant to sound like a constipated baboon or Tarzan in a state of post-coital depression, but I mimed surprised appreciation all the same.

'Terrific, Ambrosius! If I had hands I'd clap you. May I ask what language that proof of your abilities was in?'

'You'll s-s-soon find out, my friend. Let's rest now, so as to be fi-fi-fit for tomorrow's investigations.'

'Not before you've explained two things which have been puzzling me since we first met. First, how you learnt to write, and second, why you said you were a seeker after knowledge in the field of ESP.'

'The t-t-two are closely connected. But it's easier to explain the wr-wr-writing than you may think. There came a point when I had to l-l-learn to record what I knew, because of the extent my studies of ESP were assuming. So I looked over Diana's sh-sh-shoulder and practised on the quiet, until one day it worked. Of course she doesn't know. I hide my ma-ma-manuscripts in a hurry as soon as d-d-day dawns and she gets sick of her own artistic efforts.'

'ESP. Extra-sensory perception. Forms of perception other than by the normal senses, such as telepathy, clairvoyance and prophecy, the subject of parapsychological research, right?'

'My t-t-turn to applaud you! But whereas the abbreviation usually stands for the extra-sensory abilities of the human psyche, my research goes the other way, s-s-so to speak: ma-ma-manifestations of ESP in animals, also known as animal psi re-re-research. Animals have often behaved strangely in the pr-pr-presence of ghosts, or when their owners die, and there are well do-do-documented cases of "psi-trailing", the phenomenon of an animal left be-be-behind by its master who travels great distances to find him, through districts it has never seen before.'[10]

Well, well, well! I couldn't wait to hear what came next. Probably a UFO to take Diana and her psi-pussy off on a shuttle flight to Andromeda. To be honest, I was getting thoroughly fed up with all this hocus-pocus. Had I landed up in some course on esotericism for burnt-out managers? And yet . . . my mind, now working at furious speed, was gradually beginning to entertain the uncomfortable feeling that all these bizarre pieces of the jigsaw belonged together in a way I still didn't understand and that some time, when they were all fitted into each other, they'd show a picture which explained everything. I also suspected that Ambrosius would play no small part in this final jelling process. Perhaps, I said to myself, perhaps he should have put his own name at the top of the list and added an exclamation mark.

'You leave me speechless with amazement again, Ambrosius. In the course of my life I've met many extraordinary members of our species, but you outshine them all with your remarkable abilities. Just why have you gone in for such a way-out branch of science?'

Ambrosius smiled proudly and began an extended stretching and back-arching exercise. In the process, his sharp claws perforated the paper under them and crumpled it. I was suddenly dazzled by the beauty and flexibility of his body, which was still very vigorous. The shimmering sorrel of his coat, a warm and lustrous apricot-pink spreading like a ghostly shadow to cloak him from back to feet, did in fact make him look rather like some wise old scholar. In mild contrast to his almost flesh-coloured back, his front was a dull creamy white from his lower jaw down to his belly, so that all things considered he looked like some improbable optical illusion. His eyes, half closed as he stretched and as if illuminated from within, were the eyes of a magician with a mysterious smile doing his very best trick. But my vague feeling that he'd sold his soul to the devil for something unspeakable was growing stronger and stronger.

'W-w-way-out? Depends on your point of view. But your surprise shows how r-r-ready we are to adopt humanity's in-in-infatuation with cold reason, Francis. We've ab-ab-absorbed a mechanistic view of the world as seen by unimaginative idiots, with the brain regarded as a kind of pocket cal-cal-calculator and the body as coachwork that can always be repaired. A pity, a pity. But even d-d-dry science now admits how little it really knows. In-in-instinct's the magic word that's supposed to explain our behaviour. In co-co-connection with our kind, they mention it sometimes with a smile of acknowledgement, sometimes with b-b-barely veiled arrogance. We're supposed to have the instinct, the hu-hu-humans have the clear intellect. How simple their co-co-complicated world really is, though! Just occasionally, when they hear a few n-n-nasty facts about their species, for instance how there'll soon be ten billion of them on this fragile little pl-pl-planet and no appeal to reason can stop this urge to se-se-self-destruction, just occasionally they get a vague feeling that even their intellect can't be any great shakes. Now I see instinct as a direct hot line to an almighty be-be-being permeating all creation with a glowing current of power. Call it nature, the spirit of the earth, even Go-Go-God if you like. I discovered this aspect of our na-na-nature through close contact with the other forest dwellers. I was struck by the se-se-sensitive, in fact clairvoyant way their internal antennae responded to danger, finding food, the approach of death. So I studied the lit-lit-literature on the subject until it all made sense. Did you know that in the d-d-days of classical antiquity the Greeks and Romans drew conclusions about the future from observing birds, their flight, their feeding ha-ha-habits and their calls, and by examining the entrails of sacrificed animals? Our own kind has more intensive access to p-p-paranormal abilities than any other creature. We are all ou-ou-outstanding mediums. It's been shown that we can foresee volcanic eruptions, severe thunderstorms and earthqu-qu-quakes. When the city of Pompeii perished, buried in a stream of lava, not a single classical member of our species was found in the ruins – but any number of do-do-dogs! We were per-per-persecuted in the Middle Ages for our prophetic talents, and burnt alive by superstitious Christians who thought we had supernatural knowledge. And my word, those ba-ba-barbarians came pretty close to the truth. Be that as it may, my own field is the future, Francis, and I'm experimenting with various ways of ma-ma-making it visible.'

I took a deep breath while at the same time contemplating an extremely terrestrial phenomenon, to wit how much humans and their domestic pets resemble each other, and not just in point of physiognomy either. Or was it living together that made them turn out that way? With our chief rivals, dogs, the fact is so obvious that there's no need to argue about it. And now it was happening to us too! At least, after this sermon on psi powers I was having some difficulty in deciding which was the crazier, Diana or Ambrosius. Somehow or other, it seemed, the forest had turned them into present-day dervishes who thought more of the swing of a divining rod than of the collapse of Communism. Next moment it occurred to me that outsiders probably thought just the same of Gustav and me in the days of our happy life together, i.e. that we looked amazingly like each other. Not only did the notion instantly turn my stomach, it then made me feel like sinking into the ground for shame.

'I must admit there's something intriguing about your subject, Ambrosius. I just don't believe in it. OK, so I do get nasty presentiments quite often, and my instinct is practically infallible. But you couldn't say I had clairvoyant gifts. For instance, my home is miles away, and with the best will in the world I couldn't find my way back to it. So where does that leave your extra-sensory direction-finding magic?'

Ambrosius had come to the end of his stretching exercises, and extended himself fully one last time. This manoeuvre entailed raising his rump right up in the air while he pressed his chest flat to the desk top and stretched his paws out in front of him, so that his form resembled a question mark fallen over on its side. I saw his apricot tail winding in the air above his back like a fakir's dancing snake. It gradually attained an unusual stability. Then it began swinging steadily back and forth like the rod of a metronome. The movement was surprisingly fascinating – and paradoxically enough it made me feel very sleepy.

'V-v-very likely the failure of your homing instinct can be explained more simply than you think, my friend – by the way, do you like my tail, Francis? Sw-sw-swings nicely, doesn't it? To and fro, to and fro, to and fro . . . '

'What? What do you mean by that?'

The pupils of his eyes, right in front of my nose, seemed to be swaying in a metronomic rhythm too – to and fro and to and fro and to and fro . . .

'To and fro – now watch this carefully, Francis! To and fro – don't take your eyes off me, Francis! – to and fro – do you feel yourself getting heavier, Francis, feeling calmer? To and fro . . . '

My eyelids did indeed feel very heavy, as if anvils were weighing them down. I half closed my eyes, though I couldn't take them off the swinging tail. The movement was just too fascinating. Like a good friend waving, like blades of grass blowing in the wind before a beautiful sunset sky. All the same, the last wakeful part of my mind uttered a criticism, if a very muted one, of all this overpowering harmony.

'What do you mean by that, you devil?' I almost whispered.

'I m-m-mean – to and fro – it m-m-may not be ordained – to and fro – for you to fi-fi-find your way home, Francis – to and fro . . . '

Oh no? How sad. Perhaps it wasn't ordained for me to listen to any more of this drivel either. Perhaps it would be better just to lie down, close my eyes, and dream of nothing but the phenomenally harmonious movement of that tail. Why not? To and fro, to and fro, to and fro . . .

. . . and a bright light flashed across my field of vision. The glare faded only gradually, finally clearing to show the face of a particularly handsome specimen of my own kind. Obviously I was in a dream, because the picture swayed in an odd way, as if I were seeing it from a rocking boat. My opposite number had a remarkable coat colour; in fact it was hard to say which of the various colours peculiar to our kind was predominant. They mingled in chaotic waves all over his head, yet they were so capriciously broken by stripes and patches that it was difficult to make out any particular pattern. For instance, an arrow of bright white went up from the right-hand side of his nose to the forehead, but in its turn this light patch was blurred by marks like ink-blots from the root of the nose upwards. The pattern was the same but in reverse on the other side of his nose, like a negative. It looked as if every artistic technique ever known had been used on that face, from the broadbrush strokes of the modern Expressionist school to the soft pastels of the Romantics. The shape of his head was very fine too. His ears were handsomely pointed and had grey tufts of hair growing out of them, his mouth firmly set (with black whiskers to the right and white whiskers to the left) and his forehead high. In short, this was a very Adonis of a European Shorthair.

His eyes were closed, but as if the lids had sunk in pain rather than weariness. It was heart-rending to see such a proud figure suffering. But this was only the first of the salvo of emotions about to affect me. I'd only just got accustomed to my unusual position when it changed again. Exactly how I don't know, but all of a sudden I seemed to be removing myself from my suffering brother. Like a camera pulled backwards by a ghostly hand and swaying all the time, I moved very slowly back, and my opposite number's entire body gradually came into view in the ever-expanding area of the viewfinder. I suddenly saw a thin rivulet of blood running from his mouth and trickling into the furrows of earth where he lay on his back. This revealed something new: I hadn't been standing face to face with Prince Charming just now, I'd been hovering over him like a feather the whole time, and indeed I still was.

My field of vision was getting noticeably larger, showing me more than I liked. The subject of my observations had assumed a dreadfully distorted attitude, all four limbs grotesquely stretching opposite ways as if after some devastating collision. His body, its spectacular tabby coat shining silvery in the light of the moon, had a great gaping wound in the belly as if he'd been hit by a ravenous combine harvester. The comparison wasn't all that far-fetched, because I could now see that he was lying in the middle of a ploughed field. The blood from his injury had formed a pool around him, reflecting the sky. Occasional black clouds passed across the huge full moon now and then, briefly dimming the light and casting a pall of dark blue over the dreadful still-life before me. When they moved on again, leaving the moonbeams free to illuminate every dark hole in the ground, however remote, I saw the worst thing of all: the way he was twitching. It wasn't the involuntary twitching caused by a confused dream of adventure in your sleep. *This* twitching was the result of unimaginable pain, pain greater than the nervous system of a living creature can deal with.

However, the thing that made this vision so extraordinarily

interesting and that was to precipitate me into a crisis later wasn't the intensity of his suffering. That just meant release from all the pain in this world. Suddenly the injured victim opened his eyes, as abruptly and naturally as if the faint wing-beats of a moth had activated his highly sensitive radar system. In fact – I remember it even now – it was just as Schopenhauer said: 'Life may be seen as a dream, and death as waking.' For at the moment when he showed his glowing eyes streaked with iridescent green, radiating pure intelligence and great experience of life, his quivering and twitching suddenly stopped and an expression of relief and comfort came over his face. I ought to have felt relieved too, now that his unbearable torment had come to an end. But unfortunately I wasn't in the finale of some tear-jerking animated film which you switch off with a lump in your throat; I was in a realm beyond ordinary earthly laws. So I had to go on pondering the bitter mystery of our existence and staring it in the face, though I would rather have turned away.

Violet vapours were now rising from the open wound, rapidly coming together in the air to form a bright star-shape. When this metamorphosis was complete the magical glowing form made straight for me. I began to realise what was coming, and even in my trance-like state I tried to avert it by dint of mental acrobatics, the way you can stop disasters happening in a dream just by waking up. But on this occasion there was no waking up and no escape. The glittering purple light hit me, went through me, and it was as if a great bubble burst inside me, dissolving all interest in everything I had ever seen, suffered or attempted. There was no past and no future, only an eternal hovering in the presence of static bliss. All the same, two voices were arguing in my mind, two old enemies who wanted to bend me to their respective wills on this totally weird plane of being.

Glowing like a phosphorescent insect, I drifted further and further away from my dead colleague on the ground, while the irreconcilable adversaries of the shadow kingdom implacably pressed their opinions on me.

'Give him up, Francis!' one of them told me. 'Give him up. Nothing means anything to him now.'

'Don't go away, Francis!' said the other. 'His last hour is still far off. It will come some day, but not now.'

'But can't you feel it's better for him this way, Francis?' the other voice pointed out. 'Don't you realise it was only his blind, idiotic will that gave him the illusion of a full and happy life, when every day was really like begging for water in hell? Whatever it may look like, my friend, it's never worth it! Let him go, accept it, say goodbye!'

True, I thought, most of us spend our lives in an incredibly meaningless way, empty of significance, hollow and insensate. There's nothing but weary yearning, suffering, a dreamlike tottering progress from age to age until we die. We're like clockwork, wound up and going without knowing why. And every time one of us is conceived and born, the clockwork of life is wound up again, to play the tune it's already played countless times, bar by bar, beat by beat, with just a few insignificant variations.

However, the other voice in me wouldn't have this. 'Not everyone stumbles through life as if lost in the forest, Francis. Some are chosen to show others the way. Our friend down there spread order and harmony among his kind and will go on doing so yet. Only when you've lit a light for yourself can it shine for others too.'

The spirit voices argued more and more ferociously, trying to convince me of something whose full significance finally dawned upon me. My happy mood of a moment ago turned to panic. The stress of deciding whether to go back down or just say goodbye to him and this horrible world left me in a cruel state of anxiety; I could have screamed out loud with the tension of it all. My poor head would explode if this destructive brooding went on.

'Let go! Fly away!' cried one of the voices – a solemn order not to be denied, as if it came straight from the mouth of God.

'Don't leave him! Go back to him!' its counterpart demanded with equal vehemence.

Rising to the stars again through the warm winds of night, I glanced down at my blood-soaked colleague in the field. He now looked like a fallen angel who had crash-landed and been turned into a macabre cherub. He was a statue shining dimly on a dark, furrowed background. And yet his green eyes were looking at me as piercingly as if he were only playing dead. In spite of his condition, pretty far gone by now, he was obviously expecting me to deliver the final verdict. My decision would have been a lot easier if I hadn't known all along that it was I myself, none other, who had just breathed his last down in that lonely ploughed field . . .

'F-F-Francis! Francis! Francis!'

Ambrosius's amber eyes were bent on me with a surgeon's somewhat ghoulish curiosity, partly concerned, partly looking for confirmation of his success. The suspense slowly ebbed from his face as he realised that I'd survived the experiment more or less intact. Or had I? Was I still the same Francis after this mystical experience, which couldn't really be put down to wind in a hopelessly constipated digestive tract? Well, I told myself, life does have a way of coming to an end, my dear fellow, and then not even a shadow remains. At most, perhaps, a memory in the heads of those still living, getting fainter all the time, becoming insignificant, becoming meaningless. Heaven and hell didn't begin where life ended; that was where they stopped. Dammit, I'd never thought of that before. Well, who does?

'I was g-g-getting really worried about you, my friend. It wasn't very nice of me to hy-hy-hypnotise you without warning. But your do-do-dogged scepticism annoyed me. It was like a challenge, so I tr-tr-transgressed against my own ethics. And th-th-then, seances like this are child's play to me, so there was no real danger. But your deep trance went beyond what's n-n-normal, and even when I ordered you back to the real world you didn't react. For heaven's sa-sa-sake, what did you see?'

'The future, Ambrosius. The future.'

'So now do you believe our kind can see the future, or anyway part of it?'

'Yes, but there's no reason for me to feel pleased about that, I'm afraid.'

'Did your future look so bad, then?'

'No, just a bit dead.'

'What?'

'I saw my own death, Ambrosius.'

'Could you t-t-tell when it was?'

'I didn't look ninety years old, if that's what you mean.'

'Still, if you don't know the ti-ti-time, that's not so bad. There could be years of ha-ha-happiness ahead of you yet.'

'Grounds for rejoicing, I'm sure. But I'd advise you not to play such tricks in future, or you could lose your hypnotic tail and find it in the jar where Diana keeps her paint-brushes. It was peculiar, though. I felt death was both a disaster and a blessing. My body was hovering . . . '

Suddenly the alarms went off. I was still feeling shaken by my vision, and the shrill screech of the sirens shredded my nerves like a freshly sharpened butcher's knife, not to mention nearly bursting my eardrums. In a flash I jumped up and looked out of the window in fright. Outside, the halogen floodlights had turned night to day. Bewilderment was written all over Ambrosius's face too; he was staring as if electrified at the source of the alarm. What had roused the monitors from their twilight sleep? A bird flying low? A stray deer? Diana herself, gone completely off her rocker and holding a witches' sabbath down in the yard?

We jumped up on the window-sill together, ran down the

tiles of the roof and peered over the side of the gutter. At first I could scarcely recognise the thing lying on the ground only a metre from the wooden veranda. It looked like some tramp's discarded grey, mottled bundle. But the halogen light was pitiless, insistent in its clarity, showing outlines clear and plain and even casting light on the little details – on the facts. And so I finally identified that bundle as the being I had seen only a few hours ago as if through a cloud of enchanted gossamer . . .

Alcina!

There was a great gaping gash in her throat, reaching almost the whole way round her neck. As a result her head was almost separate from her body, attached only by the flesh at the nape of her neck. Her green eyes were wide open, staring straight at me, as if expecting some explanation of this brutal end to her honeymoon. The body itself seemed to have been attacked by land-dwelling piranhas. Covered with monstrous bites, it looked like a cushion which had been repeatedly stabbed in mindless rage until blood-red feathers burst out of it. The most shocking sight of all, however, was her tail. It had been bitten right in half, and the elongated backbone showed at its stump.

The sight was both a terrible blow and a reminder to me. Alcina's corpse blurred into a nightmarish scene before my eyes – in water-colour, because those eyes had filled with tears. I remembered her wild beauty, her seductive rolling and paddling, her eyes full of the sparkling green ocean racing by, and the infinite desire which had merged the two of us together, for an eternal moment, into a single, sacred, primal being. And part of me was thinking of the life we might have engendered that afternoon. I thought of my dead sons and daughters who were not to be. Yes, let the tears take my sight away entirely, blind me so that I need never see such horrors again! Let my vision of death come true as soon as possible, and then I could seek out Alcina and my unborn children in the eternal hunting grounds, sniff them, rub my nose tenderly against theirs. All I wanted now was deliverance – deliverance and a final farewell to a world run mad!

But at the same time I felt a fool. I'd posed to Ambrosius as the wily detective, although I had no notion of what was actually going on. Since no one would really believe such a thing of the Wild Ones, I'd offered a super-clever bit of deduction casting suspicion on a minority persecuted over the centuries. And now I had proof of their innocence. But at what a price! How irresponsible I'd been – how dishonourable! It wasn't my own tortuous mental processes that had unmasked the murderer, but Ambrosius and his intuition. Yes, the murderer had to be the Black Knight. He must have watched my love-making with Alcina, but he didn't attack then and there because he'd thought of something even more diabolical. Then he had revealed himself to me in a fit of megalomania, something serial killers with a supernatural aura about them are prone to do. And as a sadistic finale he had taught Alcina the full meaning of horror, then dragged the corpse in his teeth straight to the forecourt of the house and laid it right on my doorstep, so to speak – which meant he couldn't be far off at this very moment.

Remorse instantly turned to cold rage and a desire for revenge. Why should someone who thought it amusing to take other people's lives go on living himself? I felt as though I could put everything right if I went after the monster at once and challenged him to fight. By God, I had a good chance this time! It was all the same to me whether he, his ravening mastiff or both of them tore me to bits. At least I'd have done my duty and paid Alcina my last respects.

With a positively suicidal leap, and before Ambrosius could express his alarm, I let myself drop from the roof to the forecourt some four metres below. As I did so, I automatically turned my head down, placed the front of my body at an angle of a hundred and eighty degrees to the ground, stretched out my forepaws, spread my hind legs wide and twisted the back of my body, using my tail to balance myself. I landed on all-fours, with my back arched to reduce the shock of impact – right beside Alcina's corpse. I can't tell you how dreadful she looked at close quarters. But I wasn't in a mood for mourning now; I felt like killing blindly and with relish. Never before, not even in my worst attacks of rage, had I felt such a craving to destroy. But life, vile life, had yet another surprise in store. Or as Schopenhauer puts it: 'No one knows what his own powers of suffering and action are until something sets them in motion – just as we do not see, from the calm surface of water in a pool, the way it can fall intact from a precipice, foaming and raging.'

CHAPTER 6

Like a kamikaze diver going down into the raging inferno of the waves, I plunged into the dark forest without the faintest idea which way the killer had gone. Behind me, I heard Diana run out of the house. Her assortment of flood-lights made the place look like an open-air disco. But I took no interest whatsoever in that. I was possessed by my wish to make mincemeat of Alcina's murderers, although I was ready to admit without the faintest envy that they had more experience of butchery. My vision of death had left me in an oddly fearless state. Fear, I thought, is for those who believe themselves immortal. But in the next few minutes, and not just then, I was to discover that things were rather more complicated than that.

My instincts had spontaneously set me on the right track, for I heard a rustling noise in the deep darkness of the under-growth, a rustling noise moving away from me at the same speed as I was trying to get at it. What's more, it seemed to be coming from two directions at once, which suggested that Crazy Hugo and the mastiff had now parted company and were running away separately. Running away from me, too – what a triumph! I speeded up and began to run. Bushes and branches whipped into my face as I raced madly on, tak-ing daring leaps over hillocks. High on the opiates manufac-tured by the body itself, I pursued the phantoms of the night, absolutely convinced I could overpower and execute them. Another sound began to accompany the rustling: an angry growling, the kind made by creatures at bay. I ignored the awkward question of why two such ruffians should fear a flyweight like me; paradoxically, the angry sounds made by my quarry gave me positively supernatural powers. Full of enthusiasm, I raced on, faster and faster and faster. Soon I could hear them only just ahead of me. I could even pick up their scent. That was odd: they didn't smell at all as I'd expected. Well, what did I think they ought to smell like? Employees at the city cemetery after a rather unsavoury exhumation? They didn't smell a bit like that. The scent given off by their glands reflected wild, restless life, along with all the complicated overtones and messages which only an animal nose can decode.

The two of them . . . Two of them? Suddenly I wasn't so sure whether I really was after two fugitives. Because the closer I came, the more confused did the rustling sounds become, drifting apart as if a whole group were fanning out. Or was I suffering aural delusions caused by the rustling of the leaves which we were all brushing as we ran past them? Before I knew it I seemed to have caught up with my quarry and be running parallel. I felt fear . . . but hadn't I foresworn fear only a few minutes ago? Hadn't I banished it from my life long ago, seeing no use for it in the face of death? However, worse was to come. Suddenly we weren't level any more. One of us had put on a sprint, like the winning horse in a race, while the others had throttled back their speed in a very curious way. And of course the idiotic racehorse was none other than your friend Francis Ironheart. With the goal so close to my eyes, or rather my ears, I'd overdone things. The enemies I'd been pursuing were now behind me, and all of a sudden they were after me instead of vice versa. At the same time, my thirst for revenge instantly changed to naked desire for survival. It dawned on me, with all the unpleasantness of an electric shock, that I'd gone and fallen into a trap. No one had really been running away from little Francis and his threats of revenge, oh no! They'd thrown him a bait in the shape of Alcina's body, that was more like it, thereby luring him out of Diana's house to finish him off at their leisure. Now *that's* what I call a brilliant plan, I thought. I evidently knew my way around the diabolical thought processes of psychopaths as well as Michael Jackson knows his around the New York subway system.

Well, the damage was done, and the open-air slaughter of one stupid sucker couldn't be far in the future. I cast a hunted glance behind me, and shuddered. Like signal lights on a coastline shrouded in banks of mist, demonic eyes were blinking among the dark thickets of young evergreens. God Almighty, was there a whole pack after me? Or was it 'just' Crazy Hugo and the mastiff who could double back on their tracks so quickly they were like sheepdogs and seemed to be everywhere at once? My little heart was hammering as wildly as if fuelled by pure cocaine. My paws had become the hooves of a racehorse galloping mindlessly on, its pain numbed by a pain that was even worse. I was beginning to feel dizzy. Everything started going round and round in front of my eyes. I saw the first deep blue shimmer of dawn above the treetops. Morning was breaking.

Then I felt their sulphurous breath on my neck. And yet again I heard the growling, but it didn't sound frightened this time, it sounded full of cold rage. It was finally drowned out by a howl and then abrupt bursts of shrill squealing which couldn't have sounded worse issuing from the throats of the mad. So who actually were my pursuers? Though I was about to offer the brutes my guts for breakfast any moment now, I didn't dare look round again. The sight of them might well deprive me of my reason, and if I was going to die I wanted to do it with a clear head. I owed myself that much. The mad cries grew louder, following one another in quick succession, venting their feelings in a murderous screeching . . .

Right ahead of me I saw the thick branch of a rather gnarled tree. It was an arm's length above the ground, like an automatic barrier across the path I was taking, which was covered with ground ivy. And on this branch lay an old acquaintance. That was all I needed in my desperate situation. I identified it by the vast left paw with the last of the moonlight shining on it. The rest of the creature, a body ten times bigger than mine, was hidden in the shadow of the tree, so that the figure as a whole was just a vague silhouette. Only its ears, very like our own, burned themselves into my memory in spite of my distress because of the tufts of stiff hair like brushes growing from their tips. The creature's eyes, staring at me in silence, glowed in the dark like phosphorescent crystals in a coal mine. He was Monster Paw, he meant the end of all my hopes, and he seemed to have a wonderful knack of timing, always turning up just at the crucial moment.

Before I could whisk under the branch and away, Monster Paw rose on his hind legs and arched his upper body like a Titan. What a lovely situation: a bunch of bloodthirsty bastards coming up behind me, hardly able to wait a moment longer to evaluate the results of my tin-opener Gustav's laborious experiments in fattening me up. And ahead of me the presiding spirit of the entire performance ready to jump down and grab the first and most delicious piece. All right, so I wouldn't be a spoilsport and ruin this magical spring morning for the lot of them. I came to an abrupt halt.

Monster Paw came at me with a gigantic leap of such grace that it took my breath away. I saw him stretching out all his limbs in flight, claws extended as far as they would go, as he underwent metamorphosis into an aerial acrobat. I resigned myself to my fate. It was a great comfort to think this perfectly formed monster's carving skills would usher me into a better world. Gave the whole thing a touch of style.

To my surprise, however, Monster Paw's flight lasted longer than I expected. He obviously had some other landing place in mind than Francis Airport. The monster merely whooshed past me a millimetre overhead and then, judging by the squeals of pain, crash-landed right in the middle of my pursuers. They set up a mighty hullabaloo behind me, and I plucked up the courage to glance back. But the dim morning light was giving no secrets away, and I could make out nothing much except for flying tufts of grass and murderous pairs of eyes batting to and fro like juggler's balls on fire. I could hear things, though. The thunderous bellow of Monster Paw, the screeching of my hunters, a sound somewhere between fear and hatred, and all the time a tearing and a rending and a cracking – I could only guess at the bloody spectacle being played out there in the darkness.

I stepped on the gas and went full speed ahead. Let the forest monsters fight until they could only haunt the place as extinct species in impassioned conservationist pamphlets. What did I care? At least there'd be one pleasing side effect: the serial murders would stop. In spite of my glee at the idea, of course I couldn't help turning my head to look back as I fled, so as to keep one eye on the gloomy spot where battle still raged. And of course I couldn't help meditating on a couple of points either. Why had my spooky pursuers chased me at all, giving me such a nasty scare? If they wanted to finish me off, surely it would have been easier for them to do the deed right away, the moment I entered the forest. Or was I suffering from delusions? Was Monster Paw the real murderer, and had I just happened to help him commit another massacre? But then why had he spared me when I was standing right in front of his nose, first in line for the chop? And why did Alcina have to die? Her demise didn't fit the methods of the murderer, who preferred killings en masse. Was there a real Black Knight after all, a degenerate but crafty creature who thought he'd found an opponent worthy of him when I turned up in the forest?

I bumped straight into him. Him? Well, the Black Knight, of course, who else? Unfortunately, my observations of the battlefield combined with my attempts at deduction had called for my entire concentration, so I'd completely forgotten to turn my head forward again and avoid the danger in time. I didn't know how long I had been running or how far I now was from the combatants. But just as I turned to look the way I was going again, I found myself looking straight into the eyes of the apparition I thought I had seen on the cliff-top, whether as dream or reality. A glance somewhere between demonic powers of suggestion and a curious amusement transfixed me: I could hardly escape it. It was too late for me to come to a complete halt, so we collided with a dull thud and lost our balance. I pushed my opponent over – in the confusion of the moment he was hardly more than a swirling shadow – but he didn't fall to the ground. Something much nastier happened instead.

As luck would have it, the Knight of the Mournful Countenance was standing on the bank of the stream I knew only too well. If you ask me, it deserved first prize for the most importunate brook on God's earth. Before we tumbled head over heels into the water, I noticed in passing that just to put the lid on it, we'd picked the widest and roughest part. The moment we struggled up to the surface again, the current carried us away by main force. Now squealing, now involuntarily testing the water quality, I saw my victim in the distance, paws splashing about in panic. He was yelling for help in a most unknightly way. However, his true shape was still a mystery, because eddies of water kept washing over it.

By now dawn had cast a soft veil of copper and gold over the whole landscape, but unfortunately my sense of aesthetic beauty had temporarily lapsed. So as the sun rose in its full splendour, Hugo and I continued our boatless boating expedition, struggling the whole time to keep from drowning. Sometimes he was under water, sometimes I was, sometimes we were wailing in chorus for someone with a life-saving certificate, sometimes solo for Jacques Cousteau. The grotesque part of it was that a shoal of extremely inquisitive fish of a purplish colour swam along with us throughout this shipwreck scene. We must both have been a pitiful sight.

Finally the current became calmer and the water less deep. My limp body, by now rather resembling a mass of algae, was caught against a rise at the bottom of the stream bed and stayed there, feeble waves washing gently around it. Half unconscious, I opened my mouth and rendered unto the stream the things that were the stream's. Then, smeared with mud and wet as a mop, I got to my wobbly paws and looked around for my fellow accident victim. However, there was nothing to be seen. Perhaps he hadn't survived; perhaps he'd gone to a watery grave. One small step for him, but a great one for Felidae kind. That poor deranged mastiff would have to go murdering solo now.

Suddenly I heard the sound of splashing water. Whipping round, I saw two pointed ears coming up behind a branch that had fallen into the water. Wonderful to relate, however, those ears were apricot-pink, a most unusual colour for a Black Knight. The rays of the sun, stronger now, lit up the head rising from the water so that it looked like a snowball floating against the background of dark green. I knew that head, a bright one in every sense of the word . . .

'Ambrosius!' I cried joyfully, simultaneously resolving that if I ever found my way back to Gustav, I must somehow convey to him that I urgently needed a visit to an optician. Our poor colour vision doesn't exactly equip us to discover the Technicolor process, I'll grant you that, but even a mole may be expected to be able to tell the difference between light and dark.[11]

'B-b-bloody hell! The second ti-ti-time today I've had to take a bath in this damn brook!' said Ambrosius crossly, clambering up on the branch sticking out of the water, with some difficulty. He'd turned into a mass of algae too.

'I'm terribly sorry, my dear fellow! I thought you were the Black Knight. Anyway, I only saw you at the very last minute, when I couldn't stop myself. What they elegantly describe as a chain of unfortunate circumstances. How come you crossed my path?'

We both shook ourselves vigorously and waded to the grass of the bank, which was speckled with daisies. Early in the morning as it was, the sun had already switched on its incubator heater, so at least it wouldn't take our fur too long to dry off. Ambrosius lay down on the grass and sneezed.

'Th-th-three guesses. You shot away from that roof so suddenly I thought for a moment some hand had pushed you off. Then I guessed your su-su-suicidal intentions. I had to st-st-stop you. But how? I couldn't find you in the forest, or big bad Hugo either. He s-s-seems to have gone another way. So I prowled around for a bit until I suddenly saw you galloping towards me like a fu-fu-fury. What happened?'

Briefly, I told him about the amazing proliferation of murderers and monsters in this enchanted forest. At the end of my account, Ambrosius looked rather at a loss. But at least his apricot-coloured fur had completely dried off in the meantime, and reflected the strong sunlight so brightly it hurt your eyes to look at him. He now resembled an angel of light touching down for a rest in the Garden of Eden after a flying visit to this world of sin.

'What you tell me sounds co-co-contradictory, Francis. There's no reason to suppose that you were ch-ch-chased by the real murderers, or that the creature you call Monster Paw has anything to do with the whole gory business. In fact there are some indications that in your bl-bl-blind pursuit of revenge you disturbed some kind of innocent forest creatures out hunting. No wonder they reacted with in-in-indignation and wanted to teach the intruder a lesson. As for this M-M-Monster Paw of yours, you probably woke some old fox from sleep and he lashed out in panic. No, my dear fellow, your experiences, pe-pe-peculiar as they are, don't rule out the Bl-Bl-Black Knight theory. Far from it: they show how cleverly Crazy Hugo and the mastiff go about their nasty sneaky business, leading even a br-br-brilliant detective up the garden path.'

'So I was on a hiding to nothing, right? Oh, shit! There's a deadly juggernaut flattening the landscape, and here we sit no wiser than before. What do we do now?'

'Wh-wh-what we decided, of course. We qu-qu-question the forest folk and add up the results. Then we'll find where the murderer's hiding out and call the Co-Co-Company of the Merciful to our aid.'

'I rather doubt whether a wild boar, say, is going to stop and let us interrogate it.'

'We'll make our inquiries on the h-h-hoof.'

'And supposing we're successful, do Hugo and the mastiff get a proper trial? It all sounds pretty weird to me. The bear as wise old judge, the fox as a real shyster of a defending counsel, the beaver as stern state prosecutor. If they ask me nicely I'll be happy to take the part of executioner myself!'

'There are no b-b-bears in this forest any more, Francis. They were wiped out centuries ago. Just as our brothers and sisters on the farms will soon be wiped out if we spend much longer sitting here ma-ma-making silly jokes.'

I agreed, though I thought the whole idea a sheer waste of time. But time was the one item of which I had ample supplies just now. Or was I wrong about that too? Now that things had calmed down, I remembered my vision of my own death again, and suddenly I felt sadder than ever. Nor could I take any real comfort either from Ambrosius's encouraging remarks or from the possibility that my vision had only been a bad dream. My infallible instinct told me it was going to come true very soon. It was like a curse. Could I escape by creeping into a hollow tree-trunk or asking for shelter in an Animal Refuge and begging them not to give me away? For how long, though? Wouldn't my fate catch up with me wherever I went? The answer was probably yes. There was no escape. My time was up, like the time on a clock which is bound to run down at some time, its hands coming to a halt. That's life – or death!

However, I could at least try to bring a particularly evil murderer to justice before I shuffled off this mortal coil. That would allow many innocent creatures to live on in peace. I would do them this last service as my bequest to them. And with these good intentions, I went on through the forest with Ambrosius in search of relevant information. First we met a Tengmalm's owl sleeping off his murky nocturnal activities on the airy heights of a thin pine branch. He had a large head with a round, brown-bordered mask, and the grey plumage of his body was fluffed up. We positioned ourselves directly under the branch, and Ambrosius began a monotonous chant made up of only a few sounds. It sounded to me more like a nasty throat infection than a language. The bird opened his bright yellow eyes, cast us an incredulous glance and began muttering away, nodding his head back and forth. This got him into such a state of excitement that at its height he unblushingly relieved himself.

'Let me guess – he's saying he thinks the law is a load of shit?' I inquired, glaring crossly at Ambrosius. The greenish droppings had landed on our newly washed heads. The Somali opened his mouth to say something soothing when a new consignment came down and stained our fur yet again. I'd never have thought a little bird could have so much shit in him. Having received this merry greeting we moved to one side, and Ambrosius conducted an extensive conversation with the owl in the bird's own strange, muttering language.

I was getting a stiff neck from staring up when the twittering suddenly stopped and the bird, now lighter by at least a pound, flew away, not without bombarding us one last time.

On the way to see what the Somali ruefully called 'some nice clean creatures', he explained that in fact the owl had provided some very useful leads. He said that during his reconnaissance flights he'd often spotted two black creatures, corresponding pretty closely to the description of Hugo and his dog, slinking around human habitations in a suspicious manner. Unfortunately, however, he had never actually seen the dreadful deeds committed himself, and he didn't know where the couple was at present. If he'd fired the same sort of ammunition at them as at us just now, I thought, he might even have prevented the committing of those dreadful deeds.

In a clearing, we met some fallow deer, with the buck busy ensuring the survival of the species. He was mounting a whole herd of hinds, with lower-ranking males watching enviously from a distance, so at first it looked as if it would be difficult to get any sense out of him. But even this imposing creature with his handsome antlers ran out of steam now and then, and Ambrosius interviewed him from a suitable distance. The two of them bellowed deafeningly at each other, but I couldn't really make out whether the lord of the harem was actually saying anything or just advising us to clear out.

When we'd said goodbye and left the roaring buck to his labours, Ambrosius interpreted: he had picked up an interesting clue. The Black Knight, said the buck, preferred to live in caves when he wasn't out raiding. There were more caves in the forest than you might expect, Ambrosius told me. They were usually in rocky cliffs, with cracks in the rock acting as inconspicuous entrances. The reason why many caves in the forest had remained undiscovered was simply that the rocks were overgrown with vegetation which made the entrances practically invisible to anyone outside. They therefore made an ideal hide-out for criminals.

During our inquiries we also met a pair of ravens engaged in a violent argument. These birds, big as buzzards, with coal-black plumage, powerful beaks and a deep croaking voice, go in for lifelong monogamy – the most frightful thing in the universe, in my opinion, even worse than collecting Swatch watches or listening to *Rondo Veneziano* on disc. Whoever thought up such an idiotic institution deserves to spend all eternity in the hottest spot in hell, if you ask me. No wonder the pair of them were shooting their beaks off in the heat of their marital dispute. Ambrosius got nothing but furious insults in reply to his inquiry about the Black Knight, and when he tried setting up as marriage counsellor and suggested that a temporary separation can often work wonders, the two of them suddenly ganged up together and pursued us half a mile or so through the forest, croaking angrily.

An old red fox, weak with age and still breathless from the chase, crossed our path. At first he eyed us suspiciously from a safe distance behind a group of trees with the bark rubbed off their trunks. But when Ambrosius told him about the dreadful deeds committed by the horrific pair, in the whining and growling of fox language, Reynard's bearing instantly altered. His eyes got larger and larger, his huge tongue frantically licked up the saliva running down from the corners of his muzzle, and he began to size us up with an increasingly unfriendly expression on his face. As Ambrosius gave him an account of the Black Knight's usual treatment of his victims, a nasty notion seemed to be forming in his mind. Eventually, as my simultaneous interpreter translated it, he merely said we'd given him a brilliant idea, and he raced out from behind the tree-trunks and made for us, snarling. We put plenty of distance between us, which luckily wasn't too difficult, since the robber fox had entirely lost the suppleness of his youth.

By midday, then, we hadn't gleaned much new information. Only the idea of the caves seemed really useful. That was something. But which cave did the Black Knight hide in if he did in fact prefer such quarters? And supposing these caves really existed, a kind of secret natural bunker, then how were we to find them? It looked very much as if the whole case was going to turn into tedious routine investigation.

Meanwhile, however, we were very hungry, and Ambrosius kindly suggested a return to Diana's house for a good meal of whatever she might have laid on today. The spring sun was at its height now. Despite our hunger pangs, we stopped for a rest half-way because of the heat, and settled down for a thorough ceremonious wash. As we can't sweat because of our fur, our saliva acts as a substitute for the cooling function of perspiration. Our licking session took place at the foot of a slope covered by wild creepers and stunted bushes, which offered a little shade. Silent, wholly absorbed by the pleasant air-conditioning effect of our nimble tongues, we had settled down at a small round hillock covered with leaves and moss, where we were enjoying the sense of cooling off. I was sitting on top of this hillock, looking down on Ambrosius, who had made himself comfortable at the foot of it. I was able, therefore, to observe every detail of what followed.

Unexpectedly – and yet again I doubted the evidence of my own eyes – a little animal came strolling right out of the hillock, or rather out of a crack disguised by blades of grass. As Ambrosius was some way from the opening, the unsuspecting creature did not notice him, and went on going with the happy ignorance of an idiot wandering across a raging battlefield with a broad smile on his face. However, the Somali, his surprise wearing off a fraction of a second sooner than mine, acted with great presence of mind. He pounced on the silly creature, paws outstretched, got hold of his scruff and prepared to give the neck-bite.

'Looks li-li-like we don't need to go home now, Francis. I do-do-don't get a delicious lunch like this from Diana except at Christmas or when she's been listening to that wonderful old song "Me-Me-Memories" from that wonderful old musical on the radio!'

The scuffle died down, and now I could identify the unlucky animal struggling in the opportunist hunter's paws. It was a shrew: dark brown back, yellow flanks, greyish-brown belly. It had a long snout of a nose, tiny eyes and small round ears almost hidden in its fur. The oddest impression, however, was made by its legs and their prominent claws; they were large out of all proportion to its round little body. The nicest little lunch I ever saw! Since Ambrosius and I had been washing in complete silence, the unfortunate shrew had remained blissfully unaware of the dangerous situation out here.

'Well, I don't know, Ambrosius. To be honest, all this back-to-nature business spoils my appetite. I have this fancy for tins, you know. I do hunt this little poppet's town cousins now and then, to relieve the tedium of everyday life, but it's only a kind of sport, say the equivalent of squash to humans. But it strikes me it might be an idea to ask this fellow about the Black Knight.'

'You can't mean it, F-F-Francis!' said Ambrosius, quite heated. He looked offended. I suppose I should at least have expressed my admiration for his swift reactions. 'You won't catch a de-de-delicacy like this every day. Look how nice and fat he is! Anyway, I don't speak his la-la-language!'

'I speak yours, though, gentlemen!'

We stared at each other as if the Great Manitou had spoken from the Beyond. Was there something wrong with my ears as well as my eyes? But Ambrosius had obviously heard it too. Next moment we turned our astonished gaze on the shrew again. The white whiskers on his nose, sharp as a pencil point, were quivering with satisfaction.

'You heard me, gentlemen! I speak your language. Without wishing to seem vain, I'd like to add that this circumstance is the main reason why I didn't land up inside your wild relatives long ago. If I may be permitted to pay a compliment, however, their hunting instinct is nothing like as good as that of the gentleman who at present has me in his grasp.'

Ambrosius tightened that grasp, causing the shrew to squeal with pain. However, he seemed uncertain what to do next, and shook his head violently as if trying to wake from a dream.

'Thi-thi-this is incre-cre-cred . . . '

'Before you get carried away and do anything you may regret, allow me to introduce myself,' continued the shrew undeterred, turning his beady black eyes on me in a bid for sympathy. He had noticed that I was the kindlier of the two of us. A calculating beast. 'My name is Zack: young, unattached, owner of a very desirable residence. While my friends went to a lot of trouble to build their own nests, you see, I simply commandeered this hill . . .'

'What do you think, F-F-Francis – shall I bite through his windpipe straight away or shall we play with him a bit?'

The Somali's surprise was turning to irritation. The tiny creature's pert chatter was getting on my wick too, but I scented a chance here. Our sweet-talking friend was the first forest creature of a different species whose remarks Ambrosius did not have to translate for me. Perhaps I might learn more at first hand.

The prospect of his imminent journey to mouse heaven didn't seem to bother Zack in the least. Far from it: he kept on chattering away like a wound-up talking doll.

'May I point out, sir, that you'd be making a mistake by eating me, and one in literally very bad taste? There's a distinct difference between house mice and fieldmice and my own kind. Our glands give off a scent which the sensitive stomachs of your own species find nauseating. That's because we contain amino acids which are good for us but bad for you. Unlike other mice, we eat insects, so our diet has a very high protein content. And carnivorous animals generally like the taste of herbivores much better than the taste of other carnivores.'

Ambrosius was having a fit of furious trembling which was getting more and more violent, and now seemed to have reached its peak. He dug his carnassials into the shrew's fur and finally prepared to give the neck-bite.

'Just one question, Professor,' he said. 'A chi-chi-chicken will run about for a while after its head has been cut off. So tell me, is the real di-di-difference between you and other m-m-mice that when I've torn yours off you'll still go on talking?'

Obviously the shrew didn't for a moment doubt that he'd survive. He seemed miffed more than anything.

'I don't understand your threatening attitude, sir,' he said huffily. 'We learn from childhood to draw the attention of your kind to this fact if we ever get into my present situation. I mean, it won't do you any good at all to kill me.'

'M-m-maybe not,' said Ambrosius, with a chilly smile. 'But unfortunately it's n-n-not Mr Spock's twin brothers you've met, it's the Kl-Kl-Klingons. Just your bad luck.'

He raised his head, opened his jaws as wide as they would go so that his four fangs glittered like oriental daggers, and gave a venomous hiss. The dear little shrew's fate was sealed.

'Ever heard of the Black Knight, little one?' I asked, intervening at the last moment. Ambrosius's fatal hiss was stifled in his throat.

'Seen him rather than heard of him,' said the shrew, chirpy as you please, totally unaware that I'd just saved his life. Amazingly, the daft creature really did think he was immortal.

'Have you had many sightings of him, then?'

'Not as many as some of the other forest-dwellers claim to have had. I mean, you don't expect a creature of legend to cross your path every day, do you? Contradiction in terms, see? It wouldn't be a creature of legend any more. But a rumour's like a collecting tin, everyone feels obliged to add his mite. There comes a point where the tiny grain of truth becomes a lie, and the lie becomes a generally accepted truth in its own turn. It's a fact that some of the forest folk have met the Black Knight on occasion, but only at a distance. And no one's ever had a sight of him doing the bloody murders he's said to commit. According to eyewitness reports, he's always seen standing on a high place, as if to reinforce his own legend that way. I, however, have seen him at close quarters . . . '

'We already kn-kn-know what he looks like,' said Ambrosius crossly. 'You don't seem good for anything but fi-fi-filling my stomach after all.' With which he opened his jaws again, ready to strike.

'Just a moment, Ambrosius. Hang on! He may have other important details to tell us. Okay, Zack, so you saw the Black Knight at close quarters. What exactly did he look like?'

'Well, like you two. With black fur, of course. A bit shaggy, like your friend who won't listen to reason and wants to try out his perfect teeth on me. But there was something odd about the alleged monster's coat. It shone. As if it had a very high fat content, or was just wet.'

'Ca-ca-can I get it over with now, Francis? I really can't sit and listen to this stu-stu-stupid dissertation on fur any longer.'

It was Ambrosius getting on my wick now. Why must he insist on practising his hunting instincts on our best witness, of all people? I'd have expected more self-control of an intellectual. Ignoring his childish urging, I went on with the interrogation.

'So how about the mastiff, Zack?'

'Mastiff?'

'Well, the dog the Black Knight was riding.'

'Sorry, don't know what a dog is. Or a mastiff. We don't live as long as you, see? Not long enough to get to know all the animals.'

'But he was riding an animal of some kind?'

'That's right. It was as black as the Black Knight himself.'

'Can you at least describe this animal to me?'

'Well, it was big. Much bigger than the Knight. Its claws were a bit like hooves. And its face looked – how shall I put it? – sort of gentle, as if it had a really kind heart. Now I come to think of it, I've seen an animal like that somewhere else.'

'Where?'

'Can't really remember. Our long-term memory isn't nearly as well developed as yours. And the reason for that is . . . '

'Where?'

'Let's think. Could be . . . yes, now I remember. It was grazing near a human house in the middle of the forest. . .'

'Grazing?'

'Yup. There were lots of the same kind. You could call it a herd. But only one of them was black.'

'St-st-stop this nonsense!' cried Ambrosius, digging his teeth into the shrew, which uttered a pitiful squeal.

And then a shot rang out.

The bullet struck a spot right by my paws and blew almost half the hillock away. Poor little Zack: not only had he been bitten, now he'd lost his home too. Panic-stricken, I swung my head round and looked at the slope of the hill above as if spellbound, because I instinctively felt that the threat came from behind. Sure enough, *he* was standing on the slope. A tall figure in a red and black check lumber-jacket, woollen cap with loose earflaps, nickel-framed sunglasses on his nose: the hunter! No wonder he had me in his sights. Sitting on top of Zack's hillock, I might have been on a presentation platter. He quickly aimed his gun again – it gleamed dull silver – and pressed the trigger. This time the whole hillock exploded in a thousand clods of earth, and while I was flying through the air in a high arc I saw Ambrosius out of the corner of my eye as he let go of Zack and took cover behind a bush. The badly wounded shrew seized his opportunity, turned the present chaos to his own advantage, and toddled off into the thick vegetation himself. Following the destruction of the hillock, I was the only one still offering the killer an excellent target. Again.

'Why does it always have to be me?' I felt like asking as I came down hard on the ground, although I scarcely thought such a question would deter the marksman from his hobby. Yet it was a very good question. First, it seemed unlikely that he'd taken me for a rabbit again. And second, it couldn't possibly be legal to kill my kind these days, even in areas where hunting's allowed. So if the hunter was willing to risk breaking the law, which could presumably cost him dear, he must have a burning interest in exterminating Felidae.

However, I had chosen quite the wrong moment for ingenious speculations. Ambrosius's terrified face peered out from the bushes on my left. Torn between alarm and the effort he was making to try to help me somehow, he took a step forward, but revised his bold decision next moment in a fit of blue funk.

'F-F-Francis! Francis! Over here! Come on, quick!'

That wasn't a bad idea, because those bushes merged directly into the forest thickets. If I could get there, I was almost home and dry. I started a vague movement that way – and the next bullet hit the ground right in front of my paws, gouging a deep furrow out of the earth. Before the hunter had a chance to reload, I swung round and ran the opposite way as if someone were pursuing me with a whip. I'd finally mutated into the rabbit which by now I felt was my other self.

My decision – or to be accurate let's call it a reflex action – my reflex action saved my life. The hunter kept on firing away with the breathless speed of a sub-machine gun, but I was always a paw's length ahead of the bullets raining down. And every bullet striking the ground behind my paws spurred me on to maximum performance, so that at the speed I was making I could easily have won a gold cup on the greyhound track. At last I plunged into the tangled scenery of the forest, like an actor with the curtain of a baroque theatre falling behind him. However, that obviously wasn't going to make the hunter stop shooting. Impelled by demons of frustration, he kept firing at random into the jungle, reloading at once and continuing his merciless bombardment of the innocent vegetation. So a bullet speeding in the right direction by chance could still get me. I ran on and on instinctively, until the whirr of the bullets around me gradually faded and the shots couldn't be heard any more.

Out of breath, and falling into something more like a trot, I asked myself why on earth the man was so bent on making an angel of me. Or did he want to send all members of my species alike to heaven? Was he a novice hunter or an unscrupulous one, in so far as scruples mean anything to a hunter? Or was he a psychopath blasting away at everything that came in his sights? It was infuriating the way my clever questions seemed to get no answers of any kind these days, let alone clever ones. Or was my thinking too negative? Zack had given a very circumstantial account. Not only had he described the Black Knight in detail, he'd also told us some interesting things about the mastiff. For instance, that it resembled a creature which might be found living in a herd near human habitations. A grazing animal, mark you! A dog that grazed and a Black Knight apparently building his own legend up. Very helpful answers, I'm sure.

I felt both exhausted and dreadfully lonely as I made my cautious way through the undergrowth. How on earth had I got mixed up in this madness? Spring was supposed to be a festival of joy, not a collective nightmare. Nostalgic thoughts of the Gustav era forced themselves upon me. Along with other questions. What was my tin-opener doing at this very moment? Was that *vive-la-différence* monster still keeping him warm at night? Or was he now missing his fluffy old hot-water bottle which purred even in its sleep so much that his eyes were red with weeping? Was it really worth it, my friend? Had all our years together left so little trace that you could turn your back on them for the scent of cheap perfume and a few deceptive caresses? It was a shame . . . and what about me? What was to become of me? I'd wanted to begin a new life. It had included fountains of blood and bullets whizzing by. I could have cursed my . . . Bullets? Why was the hunter using bullets anyway? So far as I knew, professional animal-murderers preferred shot. With shot, their range was much wider. If they did use full metal jacket bullets it was usually to bring down the really large members of the animal kingdom. Then it occurred to me that the gun which went with the lumber-jacket didn't look as if you could buy it in just any old shop for sporting gear either. Perhaps the hunter wasn't a hunter at all, but someone with a very special preoccupation. The thought made me feel slightly ill. My God, surely they hadn't set a killer on my trail? But why? And who were 'they'? The Mafia? The CIA? Or the tinned food manufacturers because I'd recently discovered that their products contained more flavour enhancer than legally permitted? Questions, questions! They could use me on a new TV quiz game. Title: Francis and the Thousand Questions.

And the questions went on multiplying in what happened next. By now I had to some extent recovered from my depression, but at the same time I'd experienced one of the worst setbacks in the entire history of my bitter-sweet addiction to curiosity. So I decided to visit Ambrosius back at the house in the forest and go over Zack's sensational evidence with him in detail. I had no idea just where the house lay, but my inner voice told me I'd find it somehow. However, I didn't get that far. The labyrinth of trees suddenly grew less dense, so that I could distinguish the outlines of a strange construction. I'd really had my fill of surprises today, but the more the branches and bracken swung aside to give me a clear view, the more irresistible was the power of attraction exerted by this object. Then I came out of the forest and into a huge clearing, where the thing had simply been set down.

It was a rectangular cage made of metal bars forming a mesh with a gauge about the size of a human fist. The metal bars had rusted badly in the course of time. This cage was some twenty metres long, ten metres wide and ten metres high. A corrugated iron hut shaped like a tunnel directly adjoined it; this hut must have accommodated the animal tamers. It was obviously correct to use the past tense, because the whole place looked as if no one had used it for years. Rampant climbing plants and weeds had taken it over, conquering it bit by bit, so that it now resembled a carton gift-wrapped by nature herself. Sleeping Beauty Was Here!

As there was obviously no danger here except for an acute risk of seeing ghosts, I could at least look around a bit. After all, by now I was not unlike an eerie forest spirit myself. Yes, grotesque as it might sound, your friend Francis now represented serious competition for the Black Knight. I began my tour of inspection in the corrugated iron hut. The door was missing; perhaps a forestry worker had found some better use for it. Inside, the hut looked like an office full of cheap and disintegrating IKEA shelving with a few file binders lying on them, although there were no files left in the binders. Apart from numbers and cryptic abbreviations, each binder bore the inscription: PROJECT ARK.

I moved from the bare tunnel of the hut to the enclosure inside the cage, and it was like walking into a fairy-tale kingdom. A synthetic one, though, making a very odd impression in view of the genuine wilderness outside. The interior of the outsize cage could be described as a tribute to advanced ideas of zoo management. Human beings will never shake off their old passion for keeping animals in captivity, but under critical pressure from the public they do sometimes allow their innocent prisoners a living area which at least looks right for the species. You'll find a withered tree plonked down overnight in a sterile monkey house for the inmates to climb, or a few extra rocks lying about the terrarium. It was into a pseudo-jungle of this nature that I stepped. This time, however, the stage designers had excelled themselves. An intertwining tangle of deliberately planted trees merged with a genuine proliferation of wild, indeterminate vegetation, so that paradoxically enough the unbridled power of the wilderness was more striking inside the cage than outside. Rampant ivy had not only covered all these plants as if applying a coat of green paint, but had grown up to the ceiling of the cage and turned it into a roof of leaves, almost impermeable to light.

What creature had they kept prisoner here? And why so far from civilisation? Had it been so dangerous that they didn't dare let it out? Above all, where was it now? Escaped? I could really think of only one candidate justifying such vast expense: Monster Paw.

Minute, barely perceptible movements were stirring among the leaves and branches, movements which could easily have been put down to a whim of the rising wind. Without seeming to show it – or so at least I imagined – I turned, intending to go straight back into the hut and then get away from this eerie spot. But those imperceptible movements were suddenly by the doorway and in the hut too, in fact they were everywhere. And as if that wasn't enough, there were sudden movements in the forest around the giant cage as well. Strange shadows began to stir.

The movements took shape, became silhouettes. The silhouettes became Wild Ones, creatures whose beauty dazzled me like holy light. They'd been here all the time, sitting among twigs, perched on branches, but the camouflage of their coats, coloured like the forest itself, had deceived my eye. Now they were moving. The general effect was of time-lapse filming showing rosebuds unfurling their petals. Like North

American Indians encircling a farmhouse very slowly, the rest of the tribe now came streaming out of the forest, moving in a patient procession towards the hut. The Wild Ones already in the cage rose to their feet, jumped down from their camouflaged nests and began to surround me. Soon I found myself in a close circle which was getting denser every moment as more and more specimens of *Felis silvestris* came in from outside and joined it. Then they were all around me, eyeing me curiously.

'I can't give you a tap-dance, if that's what you're after,' I said, my nervousness making me facetious. The way they were goggling at me gave me the creeps.

'I'm really surprised to hear that – I thought you could turn your paw to anything, Francis,' said a trembling voice behind my back. I turned and saw an old, old queen sitting on a tree stump entirely covered by moss. It was extraordinary that I hadn't noticed her right away, for her coat, once tabby, had gone grey, and her fur was shaggy and lustreless. There was something sad, something defeated about her expression, like the look of a mother who has seen many of her children die before her. And her body appeared slack and worn out – the result of countless litters. Stiffly, shakily, she rose and climbed cautiously down from the tree stump.

'How do you know my name?'

As soon as I had asked this question I could have bitten my tongue off. How could I be so insensitive to a mother's feelings?

'Alcina!' I said half to myself, ashamed. 'She told you about me.'

'Of course,' replied the old queen, limping towards me down the path the Wild Ones standing around opened up for her. I might be wrong, but instinct told me I was the only male present. Normally that would be a very happy state of affairs, but on this occasion something about it made me stop and wonder.

'In fact she told us a lot about you. Particularly how keen you were to bring the Black Knight to justice. I am Aurelia, leader of the tribe, and Alcina was my favourite daughter until . . . until that monster got her.'

'I have good reason to think the monster is really just a scarecrow and doesn't deceive anyone but the silliest sort of birds.'

'What do you mean, my son? I'm old, and I've lost my taste for clever riddles over the years.'

Since she obviously found it difficult even to keep on her feet, she dropped to the grass before my paws and stretched all her limbs feebly. As if that were an order admitting no contradiction, the army around her felt bound to do the same. They got down flat on the ground too. As they all fell simultaneously to their knees they looked like a circus tent crumpling up. Hundreds of glowing green eyes shone at me from inquisitive faces, and the graceful bodies on which these faces rested made the softest, most beautiful carpet I'd ever seen.

'Before I explain, Aurelia, let me offer you and your tribe my sincere condolences on the death of Alcina. I don't know just what she told you about me, dear sisters, but you should know that in the few minutes we spent together I loved her more than anything in the world. And that love will have been enough. Love doesn't even need a memento: there's a land of the living and a land of the dead, and the bridge between them is love – the only thing that remains, the only thing that makes sense. I hope the creature who brought her life to such a terrible end may never know peace of mind again, either in life or in death!'

A solicitous flicker showed in all those green eyes, as if a stern verdict had been pronounced.

'Now for my question, Aurelia: do you know what animal used to be kept in this jumbo cage?'

'Aren't the animals humans keep in cages always the dangerous sort, my son?'

'No, not always. They often keep valuable animals in captivity too. So which kind was it?'

'We don't know. We value this place as a nice private camping site, and it was already in ruins when we found it. Perhaps the valuable animal ate its keepers up one day and escaped.'

'Well, it must have been very powerful anyway, if it needed such a large run. And I wonder why the cage is in the middle of the forest, as if to hide what it held.'

'Experiments, Francis. Humans carry out experiments on animals and even on themselves. Why, you could say our centuries of suffering are the result of an experiment made by mankind on nature – an unsuccessful one, of course.'

'Have you ever seen any such dangerous animal here in the forest?'

'Oh yes. Usually carrying a camera and singing cheerful walking songs.'

She cackled with laughter, and her tribe obediently joined in. As the old lady laughed her open mouth showed battered, broken teeth with many gaps in them. Usually one of our kind with such bad teeth can't even catch insects, but I assumed the others hunted for her and served up her dinner.

'OK, then let's talk a little about the apparition of the Black Knight,' I said hastily, because I suddenly felt it was me they were mocking. 'Ambrosius, who tells me he and you are friends, and yours truly here have been making some inquiries and come to some very unsatisfactory conclusions. To all appearances not a single witness has ever seen Crazy Hugo and the mastiff going about their murderous business. In fact even the existence of the two criminals is a matter of heated debate. One bright little fellow suggested that someone could be putting on a clever masquerade to boost the legend. But I can't think why?'

'Who suggested that?'

The old queen's weak eyes looked round at her daughters,

granddaughters and other female relations in amusement, as if to make sure they shared the joke. And as if at an agreed signal, open mockery appeared on their faces too. Everything I said seemed to amuse them mightily.

'You won't believe me, but this opinion was expressed by a shrew called . . . '

'Zack!' she cried in hilarity, shaking her head with mock resignation as if I were a feeble-minded idiot who replied 'Thursday' when asked what the weather was like. 'It's remarkable that the pair of you managed to get into conversation at all with that know-all little stinker. He usually avoids our kind like the plague. He must have been in real trouble if he let you persuade him to talk.'

'I'll admit that my friend Ambrosius was about to do a little vivisection on Zack when he made his statement.'

'Ah, now we're getting warmer. Didn't your mother ever tell you that mice are born liars and will do anything to save their skins, Francis? Well, think about it: what's the word of a shrew worth when that shrew is in the clutches of two mousers and suddenly gets a chance to postpone death with a fanciful eyewitness account? You fell for a scam, my son! If you want to know the truth, then listen. We must bear some of the blame for Alcina's death ourselves. You see, we've been minding our own business for years. We even conned ourselves into believing nature doesn't make mistakes. Like all the forest creatures, we supposed the Black Knight was a part of the whole who had his uses and had simply found his niche, dubious as that niche might be. I myself was the chief proponent of this idea. As long as that black devil leaves us in peace, we thought, let him do – or not do – as he likes. We even felt some sympathy for his murderous craft, because we despised your kind, Francis. There was some envy in all this, and a great deal of arrogance. Now I have to acknowledge that I've grown old without growing wise. We've paid dearly for our short-sightedness. Only last night, when I learned of the torment in which my daughter died, did I realise that nature, shattered long ago by human agency, can not only make occasional mistakes, she can mass-produce them too. Our daily struggle for what little game remains in this forest is the best proof of it. But when Alcina told us about your accusations, we just laughed at her, and she ran off in a temper. However, the monster must have overheard us, and he meant to convince not just you but us as well of his supreme power by slaughtering Alcina.'

'Sounds reasonable,' I said, lying down myself; exhaustion and gnawing hunger pangs were beginning to take their toll of me. 'But there are so many inconsistencies about that figure, or rather those two figures, that I still feel inclined to entertain strong doubts of the legend. I bet I could roam this forest for years and never see the Black Knight and his mastiff except through thick banks of mist. At least, that seems to be the general rule, according to several eyewitness accounts.'

'Not as far as we're concerned,' replied the old queen, with that majestic expression on her face again. 'We've often met them close to – and anyway, we know where the Black Knight is right now.'

As if an adder had bitten me, I shot to my paws again and goggled at her in astonishment.

'You know where he is?'

'Of course. We know everything that goes on in the forest.'

'Where? Where is he, then?'

'In the Fossilised Forest.'

'Fossilised Forest? What do you mean?'

'You'll know what I mean once you get there. It's two kilometres to the north. You only have to leave this hut and follow your nose and you'll come to it. When the Black Knight isn't busy snuffing out lives, he and his dog hole up there in a cave behind a narrow crack in the rock. Now you're going to ask me how to find that rock. A few years ago, that would have been a good question. But anyone who knows the Fossilised Forest doesn't even need to ask it.'

'Aurelia, I don't understand – if you and your tribe know where the brute is, why don't you go and pick him up?'

It was a sad smile that spread slowly over her ancient face this time, like something sluggish, indefinable and grey. Then she shook her head, lost in thought. All her confidence seemed to have ebbed away.

'There's no point any more, Francis,' she almost whispered. 'All the values that once served to maintain order have lost their meaning now. The apocalypse is near, my son. And the Black Knight is only a symbol of it. Revenge? What use would that be to anyone? Can revenge bring Alcina back to life? And suppose we did kill Hugo and the mastiff, would human beings stop committing mass murder of us animals, the so-called lower forms of life? Would anything about our situation really change? No, my son, we can only run away from mankind. But where to? Man is everywhere. However, I must pursue the last glimmer of hope, because I'm responsible for my tribe. That's why we're setting off for Scandinavia tonight. Ambrosius says things are a little better there. A likely story!'

I was baffled myself now. I just couldn't find the words to convince them that the Black Knight must be executed. Aurelia was right. What difference would two slaughterers dropping out of a vast abattoir make? Bogged down in the details, I'd lost sight of the wider view. It was a mistake I shouldn't have made, because unlike many of my contemporaries I knew just what went on behind the façade of silent acquiescence. I knew that in our country, in the last twelve years alone, seventy million animals had been sawn to bits, scalded, dipped in burning liquids, stitched to each other, pickled in cigarette smoke, injected with pus – and they were always killed in the end. I knew that turtles were slit open alive, horses and pigs stacked almost on top of each other and driven in lorries right across Europe, going without water for days on end; I knew chickens in battery farms lived in an area of two hundred square centimetres and were condemned to eternal egg-laying; I knew a hundred and fifty chinchillas were slaughtered to make a single fur coat, and millions upon millions of animals were pursued, mutilated and murdered by hunters. I knew all that, and yet I'd been chasing a couple of criminals like a dutiful policeman in a totalitarian state where millions are eliminated without a word. What a joke!

'We're leaving this forest, Francis,' said Aurelia bitterly, 'and so will you if you have any sense. It would be risky, not to say mortally dangerous, to go to the Fossilised Forest and put your head into the lion's den.'

'So it would,' I said. 'Only a real nut-case would do it.'

CHAPTER 7

There's something seductive about fairy-tales, because every fairy-tale character represents only a single aspect of the soul, which to some extent makes things seem easy to understand. And my journey to date had been rather like a fairy-tale. I'd met Saffron, Niger and the Company of the Merciful acting the part of goblins, the witch in the person of Diana and her familiar Ambrosius, the oppressed peasants (our endangered brothers and sisters on the farms stood in for them), Alcina as Princess Beauty, a Beast in the figure of Monster Paw, forest elves as represented by the Wild Ones, and last but not least the demonic Black Knight. In fact it was a fairy-tale *par excellence*, but a fairy-tale with flaws in it, as I was about to discover.

Another impressive feature of fairy-tales, however, is their weird and wonderful scenery. And half an hour after leaving the Wild Ones, when I had travelled some way, I found myself facing just such a weird scene. My eyes still saw forest in all directions, but the dense undergrowth was beginning to thin out, and finally I stopped on top of a rise and stared. Wicked enchanters – indispensable figures of fairy-tale – seemed to have cast a dreadful spell on this part of the forest, turning it into a bleak wasteland. Where mighty trees with lush green foliage should have stood side by side, growing as tall as houses, nothing rose but deformed, blackish-brown stumps that reminded me of decapitated bodies. And where lichens, moss, flowers, grass, shrubs and bracken should have made a dense carpet, there was only the detritus of dried-up twigs and bushes spreading like a disgusting flow of slime. A few dying trees with bare branches still stood – ailing creatures begging to be put to sleep. This desert of horror stretched as far as the eye could see. It wasn't so much a fossilised forest as a dead one I saw before me.

In the distance, where the horizon ended, rose the imposing cliff which I took to be the Black Knight's headquarters. Aurelia had told the truth. If this part of the forest had still been alive it could well have hidden the rocky cliff like a precious gem. As things were, the cliff represented the only attraction in the landscape. By now it was twilight, and the sun had set some time ago. Dark clouds were gathering in the sky as if plotting something sinister. You didn't have to be a clever weather-frog to predict that the storm which had marked the beginning of my flight from town was thinking of a repeat performance in the near future.

Only a total nut-case would put his head into the lion's den: that was a fact, and so was the present sorry state of the mental condition of one Francis. If it hadn't been for those thousands of unanswered questions, I'd sooner have paid a visit to a sheepdog training camp than inspect this particular lion's den. But I just *had* to see those two figures of legend, if only to tell them exactly what I thought of them. However, there was another reason for me to take this suicidal risk. The idea of my imminent death had strengthened my resolution more and more over these last few hours. It was like an arrow flying towards me while I stared at it, totally paralysed, unable to summon up the strength or will to get out of the way. But if the arrow was fated to hit me in any case then why, I asked myself, shouldn't it do so in the Black Knight's den? Perhaps it was better this way; Hugo and the dog knew their trade, and would probably do the deed quickly and painlessly.

As I was stalking towards the cliff through the lifeless thickets, I thought of Diana and how very much she did in fact resemble a witch. Not a wicked witch, but a good witch in the fairy-tale sense of the word. Witches usually lived in the forest, which gave them their magic powers. They collected the wild herbs of the forest, talked to its animals, and mingled all the life and death it produced to make a magic potion. So a witch's prime task was to care for her forest. Diana had done her best, but alas, she'd failed in the face of reality. Human beings couldn't get very far on broomsticks these days. They preferred driving cars. Driving them all the way to their own downfall, as this graveyard vividly illustrated.

Even from some way off I saw the crack representing the mouth of the cave, which was dark and threatening as the gateway of Hades and exercised a hypnotic power of attraction on persons with a death-wish, like me. The entrance itself was an inconspicuous slit in the stone, but broad enough to admit even a human being. Although I was on speaking terms with death by now, I had no intention of making things easier for him. On the contrary, I wanted to make the Great Reaper work hard to get me. So I stalked close to the crack in the rock on quiet paws, and only when I was sure there were no suspicious noises coming from inside did I risk a glance. It was rather dark in there, but there seemed to be perforations in the rock some way up admitting daylight in the form of columns of bright light. I gulped, and looked anxiously up at the sky. Lightning was now streaking across it. Great dark grey clouds swollen to alarming size had clashed and seemed to be wrestling with each other. The air was sultry because this sinister, impenetrable brew of cloud weighed so heavy on the earth. A monumental thunderstorm was about to break any moment. Perhaps I would never be granted a sight of the sky again. Before I succumbed to the temptation of putting up a fervent prayer, I summoned up all my courage and went in.

Fortunately the lances of light penetrating the rocky ceiling of the cave helped me to orientate myself. As I went step by step further in, I realised that at least it wasn't too difficult to get an all-over view of this musty domain. It might be the size of a small public hall, but luckily it wasn't sneakily equipped with dark nooks and crannies. If Crazy Hugo and the mastiff were planning an attack, they wouldn't be able to contrive much of an ambush, for want of suitable hiding places. The only good cover, not to mention an oppressive sense of tension, was provided by some spurs of rock rising from the ground, some of them tall as a man, rather like the stalagmites you see in dripstone caves.

My anxiety did not vanish, but it was increasingly overlaid by the fascination of this hidden cave. The further in I went, the more closely I observed what I saw, the more I forgot the real purpose of my visit. Curiosity about the unexplored took possession of me. I was particularly pleased when, to my surprise, I made a spectacular discovery. The rock wall on my right was covered with any number of pictures of buffaloes, horses, ibexes, and human figures dancing about in a state of euphoria. Of course I was seeing these pictures in a dim light, and I could only guess at the original colours, but there was no doubt about it: I was looking at genuine cave paintings. I might not be the first to discover these precious things, but that didn't lessen the thrill at all. Looking at the pictures, which were executed with great care, I remembered the many books on this subject in Gustav's library, books I'd once read avidly. The human practice of worshipping certain animals goes back to prehistoric times. For years, people thought the idea behind these pictures was that the image of a buffalo on the cave wall would give humans power over it. But when you look at such cave paintings with a zoologist's eye, you suddenly see something else: they show dead animals, not live ones. For instance, it's obvious that the animals' weight is not resting on their hooves. The cave paintings show the feet of animals lying on their sides rather than standing upright. They are depictions of freshly slaughtered animals, intended to honour their memory, and bear witness to the great respect human beings then felt for the spirits of the creatures they had killed. The more faithfully the artists captured the figure of their prey on the rock wall, the sooner would its soul reconcile itself to its new home. Boy, oh boy, to think how things had gone wrong between us and mankind since those magical times!

The painting I liked best was one which basically looked like a kind of prehistoric strip cartoon. It showed a man with a spear hunting an animal with some similarity to a bear. In the next phase of the picture he'd killed and skinned his prey and was wearing its skin, so that he looked like a bear himself. I took a few steps back to get the general impression. As I did so my back paws knocked against something in their way. It clattered. Alarmed by the sudden breaking of the silence, I let out a shriek and swung round. What I saw on the cave floor was another sensation, but one of the more familiar sort. I'd finally come upon what I'd been looking for.

My paws had touched some bones which fell apart with a rattle. The bones belonged to two skeletons lying together on their sides, like the slaughtered beasts in the cave paintings, or perhaps like a pair of star-crossed lovers years after carrying out a suicide pact. Two skeletons in beautiful condition, untouched, as if they'd been preserved for biology lessons – but of different build. One of the skeletons, the top one, was the skeleton of a dog, judging by its size a mastiff. The one underneath unmistakably belonged to a specimen of my own kind. So it looked as if Hugo the Black Knight and his murderous steed didn't spring from a collective desire for myth and legend on the part of the forest-dwellers. They really had once lived in this cave, and they'd died here too – years and years ago.

But didn't Aurelia know that? Why had she said I could still find the Black Knight in his cave? And how could this be reconciled with the claims of not only Aurelia but all the other animals to have seen him? Zack had even given a detailed, factual description of the couple, faithful in every respect. And Alcina had gone on as if you could see them as frequently as outdoor keep-fit tracks in the forest. All the forest dwellers had given me that impression.

However, if my strange find made the mystery even more mysterious, at least the score was two-nil to me in one respect. First: just as my infallible instinct had told me, Crazy Hugo and the mastiff were out of the running as murder suspects because they had died ages and ages ago. Second: someone had a lively interest in shoring up the legends of the Black Knight in every way possible and ensuring that they were passed on. Unfortunately, whether this mysterious Someone was the same as the impersonator of the roving Black Knight, or indeed the same as the murderer, was a question that must remain unanswered for now. Despite Aurelia's distrust of the whole tribe of mice, I thought of Zack, who said the Knight used to ride an animal of a kind he'd seen near a house in the forest . . .

I made another discovery. This one, however, didn't set me off on another sequence of logical deductions, it gave me a nasty sinking feeling in the pit of my stomach instead. All the time I was trying to work out possible solutions, my absent-minded gaze had been fixed on one of the natural stone pillars rising from the uneven floor. The front of this spur of rock was touched by one of the columns of light, and the place where the light actually met it shone more brightly than anything else in the place. It looked as if the light were being reflected off something even brighter. I took a closer look – and the sinking feeling in my stomach turned to outright panic.

The monster's paw shone in the cone of light like a special

priceless creation behind armoured glass in a jeweller's display window. When I looked up, I saw his eyes glowing in the dark like boiling gold. They kept on staring at me, utterly motionless, as if they were firmly installed diodes. The creature was sitting perfectly relaxed on his rocky pedestal, and the real shock, to me, was that he'd been patiently watching me all this time. Judging by his vague outline, he was about a metre and a half long. He was probably waiting for me to die of a heart attack brought on by fright, so that he could spare himself the trouble of killing me and start tucking in straight away. Suddenly I didn't find this such an unattractive idea myself. I mean, it would save me a good deal of unpleasantness. However, there was one very useful aspect to this ultimate encounter of mine with Monster Paw. It solved the whole case! Monster Paw had killed Crazy Hugo and the mastiff here, eons ago, and then extended his reign of terror to the farmyards. All those witnesses who saw or thought they saw the Black Knight had simply been suffering from an optical illusion. Now that I'd successfully done my detective duty, I could die in peace.

At the last moment, however, I thought of what seemed to me an amazingly cunning plan. I'd act as if I hadn't seen Monster Paw at all. Then I would allow my gaze to wander in another direction, I'd turn in the casual manner of a walker who'd lost his way and fetched up in this cave by accident, and I would stroll slowly towards the entrance. If the monster made any move to spring, then I'd suddenly switch into cheetah gear, as we describe our most effective emergency sprint, after a very famous relation of ours. It really was a brilliant idea.

I turned my back on the monster.

'No false moves, my little friend!'

I might have known it. I had, really. Not such a brilliant idea after all. His deep bass sounded like the voice of a pitiless Greek god in the habit of annihilating whole kingdoms just for the hell of it. It seemed to brook no contradiction because no one had ever yet ventured to contradict it.

Boldly, I turned round again.

'I've left a letter with the Society for the Prevention of Cruelty to Animals authorising an anti-terrorist commando unit to storm this cave if I'm not home by tea-time,' I said, in a voice that trembled.

'I'm glad to see you've retained your sense of humour in spite of your arduous adventures, Francis,' replied the bass voice. 'You're lucky there. I've got a sense of humour too.'

Oh yes, I thought, and so did Caligula. Then he leaned very slowly forward into the light, and I realized I was not in fact meeting a monster but a Lynx canadensis, or in the vernacular a lynx, more specifically a Canadian lynx. So the creature I'd taken for a monster was only a lynx after all – though what was the difference? He had a thick tawny coat with shadowy patches. His tail was short, with several dark rings and a dark tip. Black tufts of hair grew from the tips of his ears, and he had a striking ruff of fur round his neck.

A series of deafening claps of thunder penetrated the cave from outside. So the storm had finally broken.

'It's funny you're so scared of me, Francis. After all, it was I who saved you from your pursuers this morning.'

'So you wouldn't have to share my flesh with anyone else?'

'What would you do if I said yes?'

'Pray, maybe.'

'Pray?' He laughed bitterly, as if that was a bad joke. But his gaze clouded; my words seemed to have struck a sad note in him. 'If it's God you want, Francis, you must go to church. For all I know he holds audience there, playing his own sound-track on the organ, but he's never been seen out here.'

'OK, why do you want to eat me?'

'The old, old story. I'm hungry.'

'What's your name, Mighty One?'

'Eight.'

'Eight? That's not a name, it's a number.'

'You don't say, clever-dick!'

Then he did something which was almost enough to send me into premature rigor mortis. He jumped down from his high perch, and for a moment I asked myself the very reasonable question: was this tawny-coated giant of steely muscle and sinew the last thing I'd ever see? Bright, flashing eyes flew towards me, got bigger and bigger and didn't stop until they were the size of powerful floodlights. When I summoned up the courage to look again, I saw his gigantic head hovering over me like some gloomy planet. He was observing me irresolutely, as if wondering whether his mouth would take my head all at one gulp.

'Listen, Eight, or was it Nine? Sorry, but I can't seem to concentrate on the higher mathematics right now. Listen, you didn't mean that about being hungry, did you? I mean, you look as if you could lose a few kilos and not notice it.'

'Don't worry, Francis. I'm not going to hurt you. Anyway, I ate Zack an hour ago. He was badly injured and could only stagger about bleeding, so I put the poor thing out of his misery.'

'Very altruistic of you. I must say I'm glad I don't happen to have a pimple on my nose. It would probably have brought out the Good Samaritan in you again. And how about these two . . . ? ' I nodded at the skeletons. 'Did they beg for the neck-bite too?'

'No idea. They were already lying there when I found this cave years ago while I was looking for a safe place to sleep. The forest was still healthy then, and the whole of this cliff was overgrown with vegetation, so it made a good hiding place. These days it sticks up like a bare bum on the beach, positively inviting closer inspection.'

'Do you know whose the bones are?'

'Of course. They're the bones of the Black Knight and his

mastiff. The fools out there say they're still happily prowling the forest, but whenever I turn up and try to tell people the truth they all skedaddle as rapidly as if I'd been offering them parts in a gay hard-porn film. I left the skeletons exactly as I found them because I respect the dead. I didn't want to deprive them of their dignity. I imagine they were attacked somewhere in the forest and then just managed to drag themselves back to this cave, so even in their death they were not divided.'

'So who do you think is happily prowling the forest instead of them now?'

'Heaven knows. I take no further interest in the whole silly farce.'

'Why not?'

'Because I'm about to set off on a long journey, and I shall never come back to this accursed spot.'

'Sounds as if you don't fancy telling me just what kind of bloodhounds were after me last night either?'

He smiled slyly and gave me a knowing wink.

'A clever-dick like you can work that out for himself, Francis. You don't need my help. I've been watching you ever since you emerged from the sewers, and I have to say I've never before met anyone willing to take on such murder cases out of sheer curiosity. Well, I did try to prevent the murders myself, as far as I could, but every time they either outnumbered me or I arrived too late, as you saw after yesterday's massacre in the farmyard.'

'Then tell me who *they* are! If you had a spark of responsibility you would.'

'I can't, Francis.'

'Why not, for heaven's sake?'

He raised his right paw aloft, his face twisted into a painful grimace. It was like the expression of anguish on the face of a father who can't tell his child the whole truth for fear it would send him mad. Then he laid his paw carefully on top of my head and patted me kindly.

'Because it would be the death of you, Francis. If I've assessed your character correctly, you'd insist on confronting them, and to hell with the consequences. But you don't know what they're like. They're beyond control, and a life means no more to them than a withered maple leaf trodden underfoot. Blood has become their drug, murder and butchery a compulsive ritual. They're monsters, and hatred of the unharmed who live a life proper to their species has made them even more monstrous. Their god is the god of pain because they've had to endure so much of it themselves. But pain doesn't often make people wise, Francis. It turns most of them into torturers possessed by the wish to harm others. Forget them, my friend. They won't survive anyway, because they can't adapt to nature. They'll soon be wiped off the face of the earth. A few more murder victims are neither here nor there.'

A dismal sense of failure came over me. To think I'd been so bloody near solving the case at the very start. For there was only one set of people who fitted Eight's description: the Company of the Merciful. They'd sneakily acted me a Passion Play fit to melt a heart of stone down in the sewers. But in fact they regularly left the underworld to go on performing their blood-thirsty rituals out on the farms. They used the legend of the Black Knight as a red herring so as to keep their good name intact. Very likely they worked hand in glove with some accomplice out in the world of day. And they'd used me for their pernicious ends too. The harder I pursued my inquiries out here, getting lost in a maze of byways, the further was any suspicion from falling on them. Shame and rage were mingled in my feeling of failure: I'd never been duped like this before in my entire life.

'One more question: how does a Canadian lynx get from Canada to this European forest?'

'By air.'

'I don't suppose you run a lynx airline of your own, so the whole thing must be something to do with your unusual name.'

'Right first time. Does the expression "reintroduction to the wild" mean anything to you?'

'As far as I know, it means re-settling a natural environment with animal species which were once native to it but then became extinct there. Humans want to see real animals back in their eco-Disneyland. It doesn't usually work.'

'No, it doesn't usually work,' he said sadly, taking a step towards the mouth of the cave and turning his back to me. 'I was the eighth of a group numbering eight in all. They captured us with anaesthetic darts and flew us here. For a while they kept us in a huge cage to acclimatise us. But we realised from the first that our main source of food was almost never found in this type of forest. That was a black joke if you like! Normally, we feed almost exclusively on snowshoe hares. If need be we fall back on ptarmigan or grouse, and there are practically none of them in this cultivated forest either. So our fate was sealed from the moment we arrived. When they freed us we tried to keep going on voles, squirrels and fawns for a while. But it wasn't good enough. Two females starved to death in winter. We were so desperate that we attacked farm livestock, and the farmers shot three more of our group. The three of us still left lost sight of each other at some point, without conceiving any young. We simply declined to bring more misery into the world, just to help a few self-styled conservationists fulfil their quota and get awarded gongs for professional virtue. We know how to regulate our population growth, which is more than you can say of human beings. There they go, over-populating the Earth by the billion, but no disaster can stop them producing hideous replicas of themselves. Well, anyway, I stayed in the forest myself, the only one of us left there, and since I had no rivals for the territory any more my bag improved.'

'But you're lonely,' I said sympathetically. He turned to me, and I saw tears trickling from his eyes.

'You're right, Francis, I am the loneliest lynx on God's earth. Whether I'm surviving a phase of famine or celebrating a kill, I do it on my own. I never feel a female's hot breath on my cheek, I've never looked into my cubs' bright, expectant eyes. I weep alone at night, and when I laugh it's the laughter of a deranged creature, abandoned by all, who can only laugh crazily at his cruel fate. I long for my brothers and sisters more than life itself, Francis. Death will be welcome if I can only meet another of my kind first, a female with black tufts of fur on her ears, and greet her with a hiss. This cave would have been ideal for a litter of four cubs, and I'd have done all I could to provide for them and their mother. But instead the place was pre-ordained to be my cell, a cell where I've lived in solitary confinement, and the forest outside a lonely prison yard. I curse mankind for doing this to me and my race. I curse all mankind. And I curse the God they say made them. The only way he could prove his existence would be to wipe them off the face of the earth again. Can you imagine what the world would be like then, Francis?'

'Paradise,' I said. He padded over to the crack in the rock, where he turned back to me again. In the dim light coming in from outside he looked like a ghost, or rather like someone who was the very last of his species.

'Yes, Paradise . . . I am drawn to my own kind, friend. I have no idea where to find them, but I will search for them until my life's end. Which will probably come sooner than expected, since this continent really does not provide a suitable environment for – well, let's say for any missing lynx. But the quest will give new meaning to my life, and hope will invigorate me. Who knows, perhaps I really will meet some of my brothers and sisters one day, and then we'll start a fur farm in the grand style – farming particularly hairy specimens of *Homo sapiens* for their skins, of course. Goodbye,

Francis, little clever-dick! Leave this cave, this forest, this whole accursed place and run back to your master as fast as you can, or some genuine monster may have your guts for garters.'

He turned, on the point of leaving.

'Just one more thing!' I called after him.

He looked back.

'Were you and the others kept captive in that derelict cage in the forest after you arrived?'

'No. They took our cage down when they had to admit that the lynx project had failed.'

'So it wasn't just lynxes they were reintroducing to the wild?'

'Oh no,' he said, with an ironic undertone in his voice. Then he winked at me and disappeared through the crack into the pouring rain. One more person saying goodbye to the forest for ever. I wanted to leave as soon as possible myself, too. If this went on there'd be no one left in the forest at all except for greenfly and people playing Gotcha! Yet the wish for a final answer burned in me like a throbbing wound. Everything certainly seemed to point to those blind, stinking sewer-dwelling devils as the only possible murderers, but who could confirm it for me beyond any possible doubt?

The Black Knight! The real one might be dead, but there was still whatever talented actor was impersonating him with such deceptive verisimilitude. He and only he could answer the riddle, since he was working on behalf of those behind it. I closed my eyes, switched off completely, and concentrated on the experiences that had come so thick and fast over the last couple of days. I went through it all in my head, step by step, going back over every detail, however tiny. I was often close to seeing some connection, some logical link between all the people I'd met. But then my theories collapsed again: they either seemed too far-fetched or they were obviously specious explanations devised under pressure. And there was no point in deceiving myself.

When I opened my eyes again, I found I was looking straight at the cave paintings. I remembered Gustav and the way we used to leaf through his books together. Of course the fool never noticed I was studying; I used to pretend I was just sleeping on his open books. In fact I always kept an eye secretly open, and I read and read and read. I was much struck again by the picture of the man who'd put on the bearskin. It was like the Black Knight's trick. Which brought me back to the same old subject.

Black Knight. Black Knight. Black Knight . . .

. . . black ink!

Black ink? What on earth put black ink into my mind? Oh yes, Ambrosius used black ink for his scribbling. That was it. And there was a paddock for sheep outside the house in the forest, and one of those sheep was black.

'Yes, now I remember seeing an animal like that somewhere else. It was grazing near a human house in the middle of the forest. There were lots of the same kind. You could call it a herd. But only one of them was black.'

That had been the last thing Zack said about the Black Knight's means of transport – before Ambrosius sank his teeth into our most forthcoming witness. His hunting urges had risen in proportion to the shrew's willingness to spit out ever more explosive information. Zack had mentioned another important detail too: 'There was something odd about the alleged monster's coat, though. It shone as if it had a very high fat content, or was just wet.'

Suddenly a murky curtain parted before my mind's eye and opened up a view of a bright, clear landscape. I saw before me the answer to the riddle, shining like a symmetrical and perfectly shaped *objet d'art*. Now the whole thing made sense. All the awkwardly shaped bits of the jigsaw suddenly fitted smoothly together into a coherent chain of evidence. How could I have been so naïve – and so illogical?

The Black Knight was none other than my brilliant friend

Ambrosius. Why? For a number of reasons – for *every* reason, beginning with the simple fact that only a hoaxer of outstanding intellectual capacities could devise the crazy idea of cashing in on the mystical aura surrounding the Black Knight and making a manipulative illusion of it. A hoaxer of genius like Ambrosius. The legendary figure had first appeared to me on top of a cliff. This cliff happened to be near Diana's house, so the person acting the Knight had time to get back and remove his 'costume' at his leisure. Then I'd seen the paddock with the sheep outside the house, looking like a woodland idyll. The shaggy black sheep had made Ambrosius an ideal mastiff substitute; furthermore, it was a gentle animal and easily led. The spurious Knight had mounted it when he set off on his magical mystery tour. It wasn't so easy to tell different species apart at night, particularly if they were about the same size.

But what about the Black Knight's costume? For Ambrosius's own fur was of a silvery apricot colour. The explanation was to do with liquid, two kinds of it. For instance, the water of the stream I'd heard running by, quite close, when I went over to the cottage. But the water had been only a make-up remover.

'Please do-do-don't kill me, brother! It was only a jo-jo-joke!' Ambrosius had begged me when I caught him writing last night. And he had been very surprised to find that I wasn't threatening him with punishment. Punishment? Punishment for what? I'd assumed he was so jittery because he'd misinterpreted my character; I thought he'd initially mistaken me for some uncouth member of our species gone off the rails as a result of unnatural behaviour. You do find such fundamentalists among us. Well, look at the Wild Ones. Yet the sight of him should have made me stop and think. His fur was still wet, and there was a little puddle round the place where he was sitting. No doubt about it, he'd been drenched through very shortly before. Mere imagination?

Certainly not, because what were his first words after we nearly drowned in the stream this morning?

'B-b-bloody hell! The second ti-ti-time today I've had to take a bath in this damn brook!'

The *second* time. So he must have taken the first bath just before I met him. His panic on our first meeting was therefore connected with the false assumption that I'd seen through his pretence of being the Black Knight and followed him back to the house in the forest. But just how did the Black Knight get to be so very black? The answer was ink, black ink, the stuff that sometimes seemed to have a positively erotic attraction for Ambrosius. He always dyed himself with it when he was going out to stage a performance of the fine art of laying a false trail. Next a leisurely trot on the black sheep through the forest, with watchful eyes featuring as an appreciative audience, and there you had your legend. Later on, when he'd delighted his audience sufficiently in the part of mysterious forest spirit, he washed in the stream and was restored to his true identity. Brilliant was the word for it.

What about all the witnesses and their evidence, though? What about the owl, for instance? He'd seen the Black Knight more or less *in flagrante* near the farms. But could I believe that evidence? Ambrosius had also acted as interpreter of what the animals said. He could have mistranslated on purpose, or perhaps he didn't really know the language of the other forest creatures at all. Look at it closely, and our whole investigation came under the heading of disinformation.

However, there was one small thing to spoil my pleasure in finding the solution to the whole case: Ambrosius was *not* the murderer. I didn't believe someone of his aesthetic nature would commit such dreadful cruelties, and I didn't think a single person could carry out such large-scale butchery on his own. No, Ambrosius was only a tool in the pay of dark powers; you could call him an idealist, faking things to cover up for the murderers at all costs. But why? Why would such an intelligent and likeable character choose to take the side of evil?

Suddenly I had a great idea. I knew who could answer these questions: Ambrosius himself. I must seek him out, get him to tell me why he'd abandoned his ideas about the harmonious coexistence of all animals and the life-affirming aspect of nature, and made a pact with a bunch of evil murderers. For I might not know everything yet, but I knew one thing for certain: at the bottom of his heart, Ambrosius was a good creature.

All of a sudden the whole cave seemed to me a stifling prison cell, and even the fascinating cave paintings suddenly lost their attraction. Without thinking what consequences a visit to Ambrosius would have for me personally, I hurried out through the mouth of the cave. While I was in there the Fossilised Forest had added some further apocalyptic effects to its end-of-the-world outfit. An impressive torrent was pouring down on the wasteland of dead wood, a torrent which easily outdid its predecessors. The rain was pouring down so hard that you could get only a vague idea of the dead landscape, rather as if you were standing directly under a waterfall. Complicated flashes of forked lightning shot across the battlefield painting which was the dark and clouded sky, and bathed every tiny nook and cranny in glaring, flickering light. Thunder rolled continually as accompaniment to the visual horrors, like artillery fire at close range.

Within seconds I was sopping wet, a condition which by now I could have described to any industrial tribunal as an occupational disease. I careered like one possessed towards the healthy part of the forest. Every raindrop that hit my fur was like the sharp point of an arrow, and every time I stumbled over branches I felt a cane was whipping against my sensitive paws. But this time something was different, different from the wild chases of not so long before. Something odd was at work inside me, although I couldn't be more specific about it than that. Ambrosius had described the phenomenon as 'psi-trailing', unconscious travel towards a goal in a way that our traditional sense of direction cannot explain. I'd doubted this, dismissing it as esoteric humbug. Now I was discovering for myself how the wish could become the will, and the will in turn could take over all physical control. The process was automatic. Without any urging on their owner's part, my paws turned a way I hadn't consciously chosen, galloping on at a suicidal pace. They were obviously staging some kind of revolt. Yet my rational faculty was not switched off. In my mind's eye I saw the house where I was going through the pouring rain and the tangled plants, looking like a fuzzy projection on a screen. Mysterious shadows were scuttling around the house, whisking into it, climbing up to the roof and leaping in through the window as if this was a planned attack. I couldn't identify the figures any more closely, because the picture flickered violently, as if it had a film of oil over it. But there were some things in it which remained clear and steady, not to say illuminating: eyes. Pairs of eyes, apparently like the eyes of my own kind, glowing like white-hot metal as they darted about or stopped to observe their surroundings closely.

What did this vision remind me of? I'd seen something similar, and not long before. Now I remembered. The daub Diana was working on showed almost the same subject. Luxuriant vegetation with feline eyes staring out of it at the observer. It couldn't be chance. There must be some connection between the painting and the sinister events now occurring in the house in the forest. As if inspired, I remembered the labels on all the empty file binders in the hut next to the cage for acclimatizing animals before reintroducing them to the wild: PROJECT ARK. The same name was on the satellite dish outside the house.

' . . . Using expensive fi-fi-filter techniques, the Ark was sending back pictures of wooded areas in various phases of si-si-sickness, shaded in different colours,' Ambrosius had explained, adding that these pictures were kept on the video cassettes in Diana's studio. Of course I didn't know much about the technical side of it, but I suddenly felt there was something inconsistent in what had sounded a very plausible explanation. Did you really keep satellite pictures on video? Wouldn't you be more likely to make photographic prints of such pictures, so that if you wanted a quick look at them you didn't have to run the whole tape? But if the cassettes did not in fact contain records of the phases of environmental harm in the forest, then what did they hold? And how did the Ark satellite fit into this entire mishmash of lies? One way or another I must hurry, because something dreadful was going on in that house.

When at long last I reached Diana's house, after racing through the healthy part of the forest in a frenzied daze, the scene there didn't chime with the vision hovering before me during my psi-trailing. I couldn't see any dubious shadows flitting about or any pairs of eyes fixed penetratingly on me. The house lay in complete darkness, including the window on the first floor through which I'd seen Ambrosius producing his literary effusions a day before. The lightning, still flashing furiously, changed the night to a flickering photographic negative and sporadically lit the place up with a spotlight. The satellite dish pointed to the sky like something devised by Dr Frankenstein to attract electricity. The one thing that made this weird scene look at all familiar was the paddock with the sheep. Alarmed by the elemental forces, wet through, the animals were pressing anxiously together for warmth and comfort. How heartless of Diana to leave the poor things out in the open in such dreadful weather. Sheep can catch pneumonia too. Then I thought of another explanation: she might not be at home. Was she out on one of those long walks in the forest Ambrosius had mentioned to me in passing? And did she stick to such an iron routine that even an apocalyptic storm wouldn't deter her?

Look at it another way, however, and the absence of the mistress of the house was much to my advantage. It meant I could make a thorough investigation of the living quarters on the ground floor, something I'd been unable to do on my first visit. Then, and only then, I'd have a serious talk to Ambrosius. I sprinted out of the woods and ran to the veranda. As I reached it I felt something was wrong. There was some detail or other missing. Didn't I have to take another route last night to get to this veranda at all? Yes, of course, I'd had to devise a complicated way of slinking round the back of the house so that the monitors on the roof wouldn't set off the alarm. But this time nothing at all had happened, although the electronic spies ought to have registered me long before this. They'd obviously been switched off. Which was odd. Very odd.

The window to the studio containing the huge painting on its easel and the shelves laden with video cassettes was open just a little way. One weary leap, and I was inside. As even the weak old reading lamp wasn't on today, the first thing I had to do was accustom myself to the poor light. However, those demonically glaring eyes stared out of the forest in the picture as penetratingly as if the untalented artist had actually managed to breathe life if not beauty into them. And just as in my latest vision, they seemed to be guarding a satanic mystery, fanatically determined to do away with anyone who dared disclose it. I felt fear of those eyes, and unspeakable hatred at the same time, because I guessed instinctively that they were eye-slits in the masks of murderers.

I turned away from the painting and went through a narrow door into the dark corridor. On my right paw, a room which at first glance looked uninteresting enticed me in. I entered it, and unexpectedly discovered that I'd already found what I was vaguely looking for. The four walls were lined with metal work-surfaces fitted with little monitors permanently installed, regulators, buttons and light diodes, several computers, and other electronic apparatus which it was hard for a lay mind to identify precisely. Everything indicated that the pictorial information conveyed by the Ark from space was assessed in this mini-control room. I jumped up on the work-surface, and sure enough I found a spilt stack of large photographs showing sections of landscape from bird's eye view. There were several enlargements among them. It was fascinating to see how accurately a satellite could show even tiny things on earth in sharp outline.

A bright flash of lightning fell in through the window on the left, lending the photographs a clarity which brought some unsettling details into view. Could what I saw be true? Or was I now suffering from some kind of occupational sickness which made a detective see what he wanted to see? Good heavens, the satellite hadn't really been looking for environmental damage to the forest at all, as Ambrosius had claimed. That wasn't what any of the pictures showed. At first glance, they were just any old shots of field and woodland scenes. But wasn't that an animal with a bushy tail on the branch of a withered tree? And weren't there several more of them swimming in a stream? Trembling with excitement, I burrowed further into the pile until a photograph that positively bowled me over fell into my paws. It was an enlargement of the farm in the valley that I'd visited yesterday, only to leave in panic after finding all those corpses. But the photograph showed even more. A whole procession was coming down the hill towards the farmyard itself, and it was easy to guess why it was going there in the absence of any human occupants. That snapshot showed the murderers on their way to carry out a massacre among our domesticated kind in the next few minutes. The lower edge of the picture bore yesterday's date and the time: 12.27. Round about then

I'd still have been in the sewers, eating that rat with Saffron and Niger. Which meant that the blind cats were finally ruled out as suspects.

At this point, of course, it would have been easy to identify the murderers – if the satellite picture hadn't kept that last secret to itself. For the figures in the photographs were only blurred silhouettes, often just shapeless splodges because of the coarse graining of the film. In that case, you may ask, how did I know they were animals at all? Because of their green eyes. Some of them had looked up just as the picture was taken, as if they felt instinctively that something in space was spying on them. So I absolutely must find out what the video cassettes showed.

Taking a great leap, I jumped off the surface and raced back to the studio. There I got my teeth into the first cassette I chanced upon on the bottom shelf and pulled it out. I pushed it into the slit of the video recorder and pressed the play button. At first the small screen remained black, and I almost exploded with frustration. But then, suddenly, a scene of happy relaxation appeared. Several men with long hair and beards, most of them wearing shorts and braces, were sitting round a large wooden table in a forest clearing, singing a comic song at the tops of their voices; it was hard to make out the words. They were pretty well primed, as you could tell from the number of empty wine bottles in the picture. They seemed to be celebrating something. The wobbly camera, obviously operated by someone who was also sozzled, swayed to the right and lingered on another person. It was Diana. But a Diana several years younger, a conspicuously attractive woman with curly red hair, clear porcelain skin, and a happy smile on her face. She wore jeans cut off at the knee and a worn old T-shirt. There was no sense of melancholy at all about this figure, which radiated life, and nothing to suggest that bitterness would mark her face so deeply some day. As she talked and laughed with the men round the table, she was petting Ambrosius, whom she held close to her breast. Ambrosius seemed to be from another time too: he was still only a baby.

The picture wobbled more and more violently, and finally blanked out with a jerk. The next scenes showed Diana and the men, who obviously formed a team, putting up the cage and hut I'd found in the forest this afternoon. Heavy construction and welding equipment had been brought for the purpose, and there were a number of Land-Rovers and trucks loaded with building materials standing around. So Ambrosius had lied to me about this too. Diana was not a scientist doing research in forestry at all, she was a zoologist or biologist. In fact, from the way she was telling the men what to do she seemed to be head of the team. Pictures followed showing the various stages of construction and the planting of vegetation in the cage. Finally the huge prison was complete and they celebrated again, with another merry party. My friend Ambrosius, growing larger from one phase to another, watched all these activities from the background with an inquisitive expression. I glanced briefly at the display on the video recorder showing how much tape there still was to run. The remaining playing time of the cassette was only a few minutes, and I wondered whether I might not discover more about the captives in the cage themselves from the other cassettes. But just as I was about to press the Stop button, the screen came up with a sensational surprise.

After a sudden cut, the camera was suddenly turned towards the sky. After a while a helicopter appeared, to the accompaniment of shouts of joy. The chopper, a sports model, came lower and lower and finally landed near the cage. Diana and her team went over to it and enthusiastically welcomed an elderly man in glasses. Then they unloaded about a dozen small cages draped in cloth from the hold. The cages were carried into the big complex, where the covers were taken off and the contents let out.

When I saw what ran out of those cages, the surprise was like a slap in the face – a slap for being so slow on the uptake. There were a lot of small animals, all of them still young, and I knew their species very well indeed. I'd met them in the same spot only a few hours ago: the Wild Ones, now older and more numerous, and no doubt very different from what their human patrons had expected. It was as if scales fell from my eyes. Before Diana's team began their programme of reintroduction to the wild, *Felis silvestris* had been extinct in this forest. As with the lynxes, the whole thing was a classic case of human restoration of the environment. Species threatened by extinction were to be re-settled in their former habitats. They'd been lying to me all along, starting with my beloved Alcina, who had made her tribe out to be watchful guardians of their native forest operating to a stern moral code. Tribe? How come 'tribe'? Another slap in the face! I'd been so proud of what I knew about the behaviour of the Wild Ones, but I'd failed to see their most striking deviation from it. In nature, the timid 'grey ghosts' lived solitary lives, coming together only briefly to mate. They did not hunt in packs, and they didn't form tribes either.

I tugged the cassette out of the video recorder with my jaws, snatched another one at random from the shelves, and started it playing. Diana, years older now and grey-haired, was standing in the researchers' hut injecting something into a wild female who was shaggy and thin and looked very ill indeed. The camera moved to a truck on which five dead animals lay, their eyes staring. It looked as if some epidemic were raging, something which the immune system of the creatures in Diana's care couldn't cope with. I remembered the empty medicament containers behind the house; I could fit them into the puzzle now. At the same time I began to realise that these living proofs of humanity's guilty conscience, presumably conceived in captivity, perhaps by artificial insemination, never had any chance of reverting to their wild origins. Man had turned nature inside out, and any attempt to rectify matters led to weird mutations.

Diana's features became gloomier from picture to picture, sadder, more bitter. The happy young woman of the old days was inexorably changing into a resigned researcher. And as time went on certain extras slipped into this shattering record of events, extra features that might seem insignificant but made the careful observer unbearably sad. By now the experimental animals had been let out of the cage into freedom; the acclimatisation period was obviously over. But instead of running off into the woods, where a wild if hard life awaited them, they crouched timidly around the cage, yowling at their human attendants, who watched from a distance with concern. In this picture, Diana was wearing the woollen cap with loose earflaps for the first time as she conducted a heated professional discussion with a colleague. Subsequently all the other items which had already branded themselves on my brain in a different connection were added to her outward appearance: the red and black check lumberjacket, the nickel-framed sunglasses, and finally the hunting gun, originally used to fire anaesthetic darts. By the time the metamorphosis was complete, I was looking straight into the masked face of the terrifying hunter who would now obviously fire at anything with pointed ears. And most significant of all, with live ammunition. Diana the committed scientist who once wanted to give the Wild Ones their wild nature back had become a pitiless murderer of animals. But why so extraordinary a change of attitude? And why had the nature of the Wild Ones also undergone a change, a change making them murderers who would even kill each other now?

I didn't feel like watching any more videos. It was too time-consuming, and it didn't give me the real background. It would be more useful to get first-hand information, talk to someone who'd been in on the whole sequence of events from the start.

As if I'd come under fire from Diana's hail of bullets again, I raced out of the room into the hall, where there was a wooden staircase leading to the first floor. I shot up it and saw a half-open door on the landing. Candlelight fell through the doorway into the corridor, a sign that Ambrosius was deep in his nocturnal studies. I stormed in – and came upon a scene of incredible chaos. All the books had been knocked off the shelves in a fit of frenzied rage, and their pages were torn and shredded. The magical bits and bobs from all over the world, probably brought home by Diana when she travelled abroad to study, lay smashed and broken on the floor. There were deep scratch marks on the statues of African gods; all the bows and arrows, brightly painted spears and other such hunting weapons had been battered into splinters. The whole room looked as if a wild horse had been rampaging round it. Only the candles burning in the old candlesticks were intact, standing in their usual places and spreading their cosy light as if they were superior aristocrats who could only turn up their noses at the crazy behaviour of the common people. I thought I knew why they had been spared. If they too had been overturned in the course of this deliberate devastation, there could easily have been a fire setting first the house and then the whole forest alight and reducing it all to ashes. But the forest was still sacred to the hooligans who had done this – a kind of gigantic church, although a church they had long since desecrated.

Ambrosius was lying on his back on the desk. All the pages of scribbled writing soaked up his blood and made him a deep red bier. He was badly injured, breathing stertorously, while bloody mucus dripped from the corners of his mouth and from his nose. He was waving his paws in the air as if in slow motion. I let out a shriek of horror and jumped up on the desk. His once apricot-coloured coat looked as if it had been turned inside out. It was covered with blood and a great many bites, some of them so deep that his internal organs were showing. His face looked as if it had been mistaken for a practice fencing target. Stab wounds, scratches and cuts made his once attractive countenance almost unrecognisable, turning it to a dreadful grimace of horror.

I carefully put my paws round him and raised his head a little way. Slowly, groaning, he opened his eyes and looked mournfully at me.

'F-F-Francis! What a mercy you're the last thing I shall ever see. I thought it would be those mo-mo-monsters.'

'Hush, Ambrosius, you mustn't talk now. Diana will soon be back. She'll patch you up.'

'Is that some kind of a jo-jo-joke? Diana's out hunting. Hunting the sp-sp-spirits she co-co-conjured up.'

'Hush all the same. You're wounded. And I know everything now anyway.'

'I venture to d-d-doubt that, my friend. Anyway, you shouldn't try to know everything in life, or you end up looking foo-foo-foolish in the end. Like me.'

He swallowed, and spat out more blood, which covered his chin and then spread over on his throat and chest like a red bib.

'Keep quiet, Ambrosius! I don't want to know anything. I can see you meant well.'

'P-p-perhaps. Suddenly I'm not so s-s-sure. Funny, eh? Francis, please, don't condemn them, think of them as vi-vi-victims driven into this desperate situation.'

'But why our brothers and sisters on the farms, Ambrosius? They were the murderers' cousins, more or less.'

'That was why. There was one little di-di-difference: while one lot had a life of comfort, the others had to exist in misery and deprivation. They'd forgotten how to h-h-hunt even before they were born, Francis. F-f-first the males died, because they turned out more sus-sus-susceptible to the diseases that ravaged them during the long periods of famine. Those who were left faced the d-d-deadly paradox that the forest in which mankind had dumped them was too small and too short of prey to support them all. Even if they'd eventually l-l-learned to hunt properly most of them would still have died. Th-th-that was why they got together to form a tribe. And that was why they attacked their do-do-domesticated cousins, who having no natural enemies enjoyed a deceptive sense of security. But that wasn't the only r-r-reason. Hatred came into it, and as you rightly suspected, a kind of s-s-semi-cannibalism. You see, they very soon found out that the blood of their di-di-distant relatives contained substances which could help them survive famine for a few days. So they t-t-tore pieces of flesh out of their victims, but something stopped them devouring the corpses whole. And then that became a satanic ritual, like a good old family custom. Your beloved Alcina turned out to be the most be-be-bestial of the lot, by the way.'

I rapidly went back over our meeting again in my mind, and came to a depressing conclusion. When I met Alcina she'd had a tuft of brown hair matted with blood sticking out of her mouth. She explained it by saying she'd been after a rabbit before I turned up and it had got away. Now I was haunted by a memory which cast doubt on her tale in a dreadful way. The first corpse I'd encountered in the farmyard, the body of the fat, mutilated member of our kind whose head was severed, had brown fur too. Could she really have been capable of such an act of unutterable cruelty? Impossible! Unthinkable! What a strange world this was, where angel-faced beings challenged the devil on his own ground – and seemed to do it successfully too.

'So you gave them those medieval names yourself, Ambrosius?'

His eyes were slowly closing, and he could look at me only through half-open lids. He was bleeding to death in my paws. No Diana, no vet, no one could help him now. Least of all Francis the brilliant detective.

'I di-di-didn't just give them names, Francis, I gave them dignity too. I gave them the illusion of being wild creatures identified with the heart of the fo-fo-forest itself. Sad to say, it was only an illusion; they resemble a dried-up thorn bush rather than the forest. I became more and more fa-fa-fascinated by *Felis silvestris* as the project of reintroducing them to the wild progressed. To outward appearance, I was Diana's sp-sp-spoilt pet. But in secret I found I felt a dangerous affinity with the Wild Ones, and made myself their undercover adviser in their s-s-sad fate. I read all the scientific books about them, and then began writing works of my own on the subject. I really developed my writing skills just for this purpose. The skill of hypnosis, on the other hand, is o-o-only a conjuring trick anyone can master if he really puts his mind to it. Then came the day when Project Ark had to be declared a failure. The farmers had complained to the fo-fo-forestry commissioners that the Wild Ones were attacking their livestock. So open season was declared on them and they could be shot. That broke Diana's heart, but even she c-c-couldn't close her eyes to the facts. And although she'd been the most committed supporter of the environmental programme, she was the first to change from anaesthetic darts to live cartridges. She pro-pro-probably had you in her sights so often because you look rather like one of the Wild Ones. I for one couldn't go along with such mass murder, I was too obsessed with the Wild Ones, and I ca-ca-callously accepted the murder of my own brothers and sisters. I thought up two strategies to save my friends – one directed at human beings, the other at the fo-fo-forest creatures. The cu-cu-current position of the Wild Ones was always determined from pictures taken by the Ark eco-satellite. It was simple, because they always went round together, and a whole tr-tr-troop was easy to spot. So I secretly manipulated the satellite to give clear pictures but the wr-wr-wrong coordinates and times. Then I acted the part of Black Knight at night for the be-be-benefit of the forest creatures, to divert suspicion from the Wild Ones and show them, de-despite everything, in a rosy light. By the way, Crazy Hugo and the mastiff were their first victims. They killed the couple only a few days after they left the sewers. Th-th-that's what gave me the idea.'

He seemed very tired now, indeed he seemed to be drifting off into another dimension. The blood welling out of him made a large pool round his head, as if he were drowning in the bloodbath he'd been covering up for, if not actively encouraging, over the years. Yet I didn't shrink from him in horror; I would not condemn him. It is a characteristic of intelligent beings that they learn to understand the nature and constitution of the world and then come down on one side or the other. Ambrosius was right: you don't really want to know everything or you end up looking foolish.

'So why did they spare me, my friend?'

'Are you sure they did? Alcina told them about you, and wh-wh-what a keen brain you had. With that in mind, I thought it would be a po-po-positively brilliant idea to turn your detective inquiries into propaganda for the Black Knight. I encouraged you to believe that only he c-c-could be responsible for such cruelties. Unfortunately you were always a step ahead of my fabrications, until th-th-things got out of hand. That's why Aurelia told you about the cave. She knew the lynx lived there, and he's a sworn enemy of the Wild Ones. She expected he'd take you for one of them and ki-ki-kill you on the spot.'

'But why did they do this to you, Ambrosius? I thought you were their saviour!'

'They don't want to leave any tr-tr-traces behind. No witnesses. And I wasn't wholly innocent of creating the murderous vortex into which they were drawn. They are cl-cl-closing this chapter in their dreadful past and setting off for Scandinavia sooner than they meant to. So they told me they w-w-wanted to say goodbye and asked me to sw-sw-switch off the alarm system. Di-Di-Diana had it fitted because she herself was afraid of . . . '

Another jet of blood surged out, stifling his words. As if pulled upright by an invisible claw, he reared in his death agony, gurgled horribly, spat out more bloody mucus and finally collapsed, eyes tightly closed.

'Don't die, Ambrosius, please don't die!' I cried, weeping. I still believed in a miracle, hoping his wounds might close of their own accord.

For the last time, he opened his bright amber eyes and looked at me with a mild expression, as if death were tantamount to a sweet drug.

'What's so bad about it, Francis? All animals wi-wi-will die soon. Death is coming d-d-down on us like a poisonous cloud. It's enfolding us, smothering us. And God won't s-s-send another Ark. The battle's over. We've lost. They outnumber us. One day humans will look at their world and s-s-see something strange: an Earth without animals . . . '

And so he drew his last breath, letting it out with a sound of indescribable contentment. The tears I was shedding mingled with his blood, and my final prayer with his departing soul. Carefully I laid his head down in the pool of blood, bent over him and rubbed my nose against his. But in spite of my grief I refused to accept the truth of his depressing last words. There was no need at all for total annihilation to be the inevitable fate of animals. We had allies all over the world. And even if he were correct, who gave the Wild Ones authority to usher in the apocalypse, as proxy for humanity? Did two wrongs make a right? Ought we to judge wicked deeds less harshly if they're committed by the victims of other wicked deeds? No, never. I wasn't going to let the Wild Ones get away with it, although I realised there wasn't a lot I could do against a whole horde of murderers. But one thing I *could* do: I could curse them, look them in the face and curse them. And my curse would go with them everywhere, wherever they went, to the end of their days.

I made the same adventurous leap as last night, shot through the open window to the roof, and from there dropped in daring flight to the ground. The storm still hadn't stopped raging. Rain was falling in such torrents you might have thought there was a burst pipe of giant dimensions up in the sky. Lightning was flashing all over the place, and you could hear trees exploding as they were struck. As I raced through the forest at breathtaking speed, I concentrated utterly on my infallible instincts. I thought they'd soon pick up the murderers' trail, and they did. Without making a single conscious decision, I changed direction several times, made my way through thick barriers of bushes, crossed unknown forest paths, passed farmyards where hysterical dogs barked at me, skirted the Fossilised Forest again, clambered up sheer cliffs and jumped rushing streams. I finally left the forest behind and came to arable land. And there, exhausted and breathless, on the edge of a bare ploughed field rising steeply up a slope, I saw them about two hundred metres away from me.

Veiled by the rain, they were trotting at a comfortable pace towards the top of this sloping field. When they had left the crest of the hill behind them, they would be lost from my sight. I didn't know if I would be able to summon up the strength to follow them then. Strictly speaking, the whole situation resembled a more or less covert form of suicide. If they found out that I was still alive, the last person to know their secret, they'd certainly kill me. Well, so be it. There was more of the detective in me than, with my usual cynicism, I liked to admit. And detectives have to track down murderers at all costs.

While I was getting my breath back, they had reached the top of the rise. Now they really did look like the 'grey ghosts' who had struck fear and terror into humans for so long. Hundreds of backs shone with a silvery gleam in the distance, like the last troops of a defeated army retreating, and hundreds of wet tails swung gently to and fro in time like crumpled windscreen wipers struggling in vain against the rain.

'Hey, you murderers, where do you think you're going?' I yelled at the top of my voice, and then I began slowly marching towards them. They all stopped abruptly and turned to me. There was no surprise on their faces, only something like annoyance that for all their efforts a troublesome problem still hadn't been solved. The sight of all these desperadoes gave me a nasty sinking feeling, but I'd rather have died than let them go without a word of loathing.

Suddenly it stopped raining. A stiff breeze got up, and the lowering black clouds began to drift apart. Through the gaps in the cloud cover you could see the majestic deep blue of the sky with the full moon in it. What did this impressive picture remind me of? The ploughed field, the dark night sky, the full moon with dark clouds driving across it . . .

'Don't come any closer if you value your life, Francis!' cried Aurelia. Hobbling, she pushed past the females around her. When she had made her way through she stood there in front of her troop of bedraggled and rather weary-looking queens and looked at me reproachfully. We were all wet through, and the strong wind cut into us like the Snow Queen's frosted fingernails.

'You won't get away scot-free from the last person to know your cannibalistic past, Aurelia. Here I am, and this tale of blood won't really be over until you've killed me.'

'I had no idea you could be so sanctimonious, my son. It's all very well for people living in palaces of full feeding bowls to condemn the low moral standards of the starving. Have you ever spent a winter in the forest, Francis? In a forest so heavily managed that it looks like a germ-free idyll on sentimental wallpaper? Do you really think you could survive even a week in this deceptive paradise – in rain and ice, pursued by hunters with guns, terrorised by cars, caught in traps? How would you hunt with hordes of humans looking for fun kicking up a racket with their bicycles, kites, caravans and camping gear and scaring your prey away? Would you just give a weary grin when you saw your children starve to death at your side? Or your own parents? Or are you only a conceited detective bent on bringing killers to justice however much necessity made them act as they did?'

'Oh, so it's necessity that justifies such barbarism. In that case I suppose you tore Ambrosius to pieces like a hare in a dog-race out of necessity too.'

'Don't paint the dead better than they were in life, Francis. Of course we were the ones who actually killed your brothers and sisters, but Ambrosius set up the gory, archaic atmosphere and the cult. He gave us our medieval names and acted as if the Black Knight really existed, as if he was a deity we must worship. He was so crazy he came to believe in his own masquerade. He made us think we were a chosen people, so we had a right to decide on the life and death of other animals. Ambrosius didn't force us to commit murder, that's true. But he helped us do it in every way he could.'

'It was your own idea to make mincemeat of Alcina, though, right?'

'Yes. After meeting you she was a changed character. She said we ought to drop our destructive ways because they were sinful. We regarded her attitude as treachery, executed her, and left the corpse outside the house in the forest as a warning to you. And as a way of laying a false trail too. But then we thought some more about what she'd said, and we saw the hopelessness of our situation. Suddenly we felt as if our view had been blocked by a great black wall all this time. When you turned up, large cracks began appearing in that wall, and we recognised our dreadful guilt. Gradually we understood what cruel monsters we'd become, how far we had left the innocence of the animal kingdom behind. The only thing we still had in common with other creatures was our animal appearance, a deceptive mask hiding bestial pariahs and rivers of blood. We felt deep shame when we realised that, Francis; oh, we were dreadfully ashamed of ourselves. We wanted to forget it all and obliterate everything that might remind us. So we sent you off to the lynx, expecting him to eat you, and we dealt with Ambrosius ourselves. We know it's easy to find reasons for doing evil, my son, but now we also know that survival won't excuse everything. We are guilty, intolerably guilty. And you are right to condemn us, Francis. I only ask you to remember that we were already condemned before we touched a hair of the coats of your own kind.'

Once again I had tears in my eyes. Oh, what hard decisions life called for! It was all so difficult. The sheer will to live had caused injustice that cried out to heaven, and lovely forest elves had turned into morbid monsters. So that was the solution of my case, the answer to the riddle. It gave me no satisfaction, though; on the contrary, it caused me great pain. Whatever torches we may kindle, I thought, however far their light may reach, our horizon will always be bounded by darkest night. For the answer to the last riddle in the world must necessarily deal with things in themselves, not appearances. The concepts of good and evil disappeared, leaving only my own little feelings behind. Feelings of mourning for the victims, hatred for the killers who themselves were victims to be pitied, and so on and so forth until everything lost its meaning in a tunnel with no light at the end of it, also known as the world.

I felt that events had changed me. I was not the Francis I had been before my flight. So I no longer wanted to go back to Gustav and enjoy a comfortable life, closing my eyes to all the suffering outside the door. At the same time I felt deep revulsion from these creatures, who might be naïvely described as innocent animals. A stone or a clover leaf could be innocent, but not a living creature. We were all guilty, through no personal fault of our own, just because we were here in this world, because we needed, rejected, loved and killed each other. No, I would turn my back on the incomprehensible world and content myself with a hermit's life. All I wanted was to go back to the lynx's cave and spend the rest of my life in obscurity there.

However, a sober look at my surroundings induced severe doubts of my ability to achieve this reclusive ambition. I suddenly noticed that my present location was the precise scene of my vision of death: the field apparently going on and on to infinity, the silvery light of the full moon broken only by stray black clouds. My God, this was it. I was going to be torn into blood-stained mincemeat by hundreds of claws. What a way to go!

This fear, in its turn, was immediately nipped in the bud when the Wild Ones did something I hadn't for a moment expected. First Aurelia and then all the sisters of her tribe began moving slowly backwards, as if at a signal. Were they really so scared of me? Or were they perhaps more afraid of themselves, feeling tempted to try instant elimination of the last person who might interfere with their journey, thus breaking with the past once and for all? But that would mean they'd really suffered a change of heart and didn't want to solve their problems by force any more.

'Francis, you must have heard the tales of old or sick elephants who go to a certain spot when they feel death approaching,' said Aurelia, as she carefully put one paw behind another, just like all the other Wild Ones behind her. Half the company had already disappeared over the brow of the hill. I stood there in the middle of the field, watching them in silence.

'Such places are called elephants' graveyards. The place

where we are going is said to have more prey animals than this dark land of misfortune, and the human population is lower. But more likely, much more likely, it will be our graveyard. We still don't really know how to hunt and lead the natural life of our species. So basically we're on the way to our death. But come what may, good fortune or bad, we're never going to injure anyone but our proper prey again. We are leaving madness and murder behind, and we hope that for all our sins, an unspoiled nature will take us to its heart.'

All the Wild Ones except Aurelia had now gone over the top of the hill and were out of my sight. Aurelia stopped there on the crest of the field, giving me a long look from grey-green eyes in which all hope was extinguished. Behind her, a cloud drifted away, exposing the huge moon whose reflected silvery light made Aurelia only a silhouette. Then, suddenly, she got up on her hind legs and reached out her forepaws as if to embrace me from afar.

'Francis, my son!' she cried, sobbing, and I burst into copious tears myself. 'Forgive us! Forgive us, my son! Forgive us!'

'There's nothing to forgive!' I called back. 'May God forgive you – or all the innocent creatures you've butchered, if you ever meet them again. I came here to curse you, but now I know you were cursed already, long ago. I don't wish you luck, but I don't wish you hell on earth either. Go in peace, and show respect for life!'

'If you don't want to wish us luck, then remember us in your prayers, Francis. Goodbye, my son!'

A hesitant wave, a hobbling jump, and she too had gone over the top of the hill. In the place where she had been standing a moment ago there was now nothing but the light of the bloated moon, and another dark cloud slowly drifting over it.

'The best prayer I can say is to wish all living creatures free from pain,' I whispered, and I stayed there for quite a while, gazing listlessly at the silvery moonlight. So my vision of death hadn't come true in the end, which seemed to show that Ambrosius was right in saying the hypnotic seance and its alarming effects were just a conjuring trick. Of course the death I'd seemed to see predicted could still catch up with me somewhere similar at a later date. But I felt very strongly that it would happen either here and now, or in some section of my life which was entirely unknown to me.

Still feeling affected by recent sad events, I longed for nothing but the safety of the cave in the Fossilised Forest. From this day on, that lonely spot should be my protective capsule against the filthy stink of the world. I would meditate there on the last mysteries of life, in intensive conversation with my atrophied instincts. Nor would I cease from trying to discover who created everything, probably including evil.

I turned my eyes away from the moon, which was shining as if it had been polished, and wiped the tears from my eyes with my paw. Then I turned round, and was shot . . .

. . . and died.

CHAPTER 8

Diana had arrived too late. Her last efforts to find the murderous rabble before they disappeared in the direction of Scandinavia had not been altogether successful. Presumably the satellite pictures had shown the unusual migration movement, and despite the filthy weather Diana had immediately set off after the Wild Ones. But instead of getting the whole bunch of them in her sights, somewhere offering a good vantage point, she picked off just one, and that one a red herring.

The red herring in question was a certain detective by the name of Francis who had just decided to change his profession to that of hermit. Was? Had? In fact, in my present state time no longer meant anything. And a bullet from Diana's gun had landed me in that state. A case of mistaken identity with what you might call dramatic consequences. I hadn't even really registered being hit; I just noticed a sudden quivering in my body before my paws momentarily left the ground, and then my legs crumpled like the limbs of a rubber doll. I tumbled over on my back, unable to move.

Everything else happened just as it had in my vision of death, or rather almost, for unlike that brief scene, with which we're already familiar, this one had a sequel. While I lay there in enforced immobility, obliged to watch the moon shining behind dark clouds with my eyelids half closed, the pain began, and it was bad. I felt as if all my nerve endings had been shifted outside me, and some inspired sadist was scrubbing them with a wire brush. All I wanted was a quick death. I squinted down at myself out of the corner of one eye and saw that I was losing a lot of blood. A pool of it had already formed around me. Then an involuntary twitching went through me; it couldn't relieve the pain, but it did take my mind off it to some extent. After a while the twitching stopped too. At the same time, so did everything that had once been of any significance.

As if they'd turned off the torture machine, all my pain suddenly vanished. Violet swathes of light surrounded my body, giving it a bright aura. What a wonderful feeling, being permeated by this magical light as if by water from a sacred spring. I didn't have long to wait for the next miracle. I found myself rising very gradually from the ground while rotating slowly round my own axis. There was something infinitely pleasing about all these gentle movements. When my face was fully turned to the ploughed field I could see what was happening down on earth. But nothing much seemed to be going on. There lay Francis in a broad furrow of the field, with a bleeding wound in his belly, twitching with pain. All of a sudden he opened his eyes and went rigid, like a phased shot in a film. So I'd been able to witness my own death from outside my body. How exciting!

I floated onwards and upwards, moving further and further from the corpse, and the smaller the husk of Francis down on earth looked, the more unimportant and trivial were those little problems and notions that had given him the illusion of life for an infinitesimally short time. You have to be old, I thought, you have to have lived a long time before you realise how short life is. And whatever happiness you've had, there's never really any denying the pain that life entails. My fearing death so much all the same only went to show what a will to live I'd had: I was nothing but that will, I'd known nothing else.

Suddenly I became aware of having been appointed arbitrator in a heated debate. That struck a familiar chord too; after all, I'd already heard those voices arguing vehemently during my vision of death. However, this time they weren't engaged in a proper dialogue, but symbolised two opposing forces in my soul. One force insisted on the power of the will and on life, the other on the pointlessness of all earthly things and on deliverance. It seemed that I didn't have much time to make up my mind, because by now I was so far from the field that the bleeding figure of Francis looked no larger than a tiny dot. As I rose to the firmament at the leisurely pace of a hot-air balloon, I saw Diana emerge from the darkness and stride across the field towards the corpse, her gun lowered.

Although I was so far away, I could see the burning question in the open eyes of my corporeal counterpart. Francis was looking intently at me. Come on, mate, he seemed to be saying, make up your mind, don't keep me in suspense. I thought about it. My hovering motion was like being asleep but fully conscious, soothing and rapturous at once. The world below was a dark spot, full of warriors fighting pointlessly in an unjust war with no prospects of either victory or peace at the end of it. And yet . . . and yet there were still a few knots I'd have liked to untangle, a few things I'd have liked to try, a few parts of life I'd have liked to live . . .

No! What was over was over. I'm letting go of you, life, I cried, I'm turning away from you. And as my cry died away in the depths of the sky I found I could not only float on upwards but also fly in all directions, as naturally as a happy dreamer. I flew over poor dead Francis, who had come to a pretty silly end when you stopped to think of it, I flew over fields and meadows, I cut capers, I performed breathtaking aerial acrobatics with all paws outstretched. The earth raced by below me at incredible speed, giving me one last look at all those who'd once meant something to me. I saw the Wild

Ones padding silently and thoughtfully towards the northern forests in the grey light of dawn. I sailed down, almost touching them, and they all raised their heads at once with a bitter smile, as if they felt my soul near them. But my swift flight allowed no lingering. Many kilometres further on, in a rocky landscape, I saw Eight the lynx on his way north too, and I hoped with all my heart that he would have enough strength left to cross the Arctic Circle and reach his beloved Canada. When he became aware of my spiritual presence he stopped and glanced up, and he too smiled, but not bitterly like the Wild Ones: he smiled as you might at an aviator friend who's just performed a particularly daring aerial manoeuvre.

Sad at heart, I said goodbye to him and steered a course for the forest. The red light of morning turned this tamed jungle to a magnificent sea of flames, its busy inhabitants visible against that bright background. Such a thing was impossible in the normal way, but I could make out every single one of them with amazing clarity. There they all were: wandering spiders, forest crickets, Roman snails, rhinoceros beetles, hornet clear-wings, butterflies in breathtaking variety, wasps, spotted salamanders, leaf frogs, sand lizards, slow-worms, hedgehogs, bats, rabbits, beavers, marmots, yellow-necked mice, badgers, raccoons, pine martens, wild boar, deer. And above them, as if offering me their services as aerial pilots, swarmed the forest air force: buzzards, falcons, hobby hawks, woodcocks, turtle doves, eagle owls, long-eared owls, nightjars, spotted woodpeckers, wrens, nightingales, robins, blackbirds, bluetits, finches, starlings and ravens. The sight of them filled me with great joy, and I wished them and any others who had escaped my excited gaze all the luck in the world.

Then I flew over the house in the forest, which still contained the corpse of Ambrosius although his soul had flown. Soon I'd meet that soul again in a happier place and engage in passionate discussions of spiritualism with it. I'd be at a disadvantage, of course, Ambrosius having known a lot more about the subject than me while still alive. After passing the gigantic cage from the environmental project, which would surely be so overgrown by plants some day that it really would merge with its surroundings, I came to the Fossilised Forest. But the sight of this ominous monument to human stupidity only made me feel angry, so I let myself fly down in the healthy part of the forest and straight into the drainpipe through which I had once clambered out of the sewers. Like a ball whizzing aimlessly about in a games machine in an arcade, I spent some time flitting through the labyrinthine windings of the sewage system, which was as clammy and funereal as ever. I finally found the Company of the Merciful in an apparently endless branch of the sewers where they were hunting rats in a pack, like fishermen of prehistoric times. I saw Saffron, Niger, and all the other grubby, blind cats splashing stormily in the water and regularly emerging with prey in their mouths. It was a pity I hadn't been able to bring them the news that there would be no more serial murders. However, they all stopped catching rats as I flew overhead, and preserved a solemn silence. I was obviously still present to their minds, at least as a distant memory or a salutary premonition. I blessed them all and then left the sewers at the main inlet.

High above the city, I saw the old building where Gustav had his little ground-floor flat, and at last, at last I saw my home range again. I immediately prepared to nose-dive, but the closer I came to that familiar spot the more clearly I saw a heart-rending scene. Gustav was standing on the terrace looking out sadly over the garden. He then broke into miserable sobs. There was no mistaking it: he was mourning his lost pet, whose silent absence was stronger than his invisible presence here in his place of origin. My old friends were in view, playing in the nearby gardens. I saw old Bluebeard the cripple, Kong the local tyrant and his two bodyguards Herrmann and Herrmann, the eccentric Jesaja, the bewitching Nhozemphtekh, my companion of so many nights of steamy passion, and several more of the old gang.

You shouldn't have hurt my feelings, fat slob, I told Gustav from the spirit world, near tears myself. You ought to have known love can't be parcelled out just like that. I loved you the way you were, with all your faults and revolting habits (like your nasty way of smacking your lips and gargling whenever you took a sip of wine). But you betrayed our friendship for a deceptive vision of domestic bliss. No human being deserves to keep an animal unless he understands that he himself is an animal at bottom, so he should treat us the way he treats his own kind. But let the veil of oblivion fall on your sins, my dear Gustav, and may the memory of our happy days together console us both for adversity. So farewell, strong guardians of the range, and my spineless friend too! God in his infinite goodness will reunite us some time, when earthly existence no longer weighs heavy on us and the ridiculous difference between species is no more!

As I spoke these words of farewell – or was I only thinking them? – I shot up to the sky like a rocket, and out of the corner of my eye I could see that the mournful figure of Gustav, and my former friends too, all raised their heads as if a signal had been given and looked sadly after me. At lightning speed, I broke through the troposphere, the stratosphere, the ionosphere, the exosphere, the chemosphere and finally the atmosphere, the familiar topography of earth losing its outlines faster and faster and merging into a vast blue globe veiled by white vapour. How amazingly lovely and peaceful the planet looked when you saw it from afar like an intergalactic explorer. Weightless, free of all cares, I circumnavigated the globe in breathless flight until continent after continent was racing by below me, and the circle finally reached completion above that part of Earth where the triumphal march of the Felidae once began: Africa. It was time to say farewell to this strangely contradictory world now, for I suddenly felt a mysterious power drawing me into the depths of the cosmos. I sketched a goodbye wave, turned my back on life once and for all, and plunged into the sea of stars.

Faster and faster, myriads of suns and planets shot by me, revealing fascinating views of their burning, desolate, icy, fluid or green surfaces, until the speed of my flight was such that the stars became mere streaks of radiance. Suddenly, right in the middle of this hypnotic panorama, a dazzling, sparkling light appeared, getting bigger and bigger. Within a fraction of a second it filled my entire view, and I plunged into this tunnel of light with joyful awe. Stars, glowing and dimming, flowed through this magic tube of radiance and kept me company in my swift flight. After a while I could finally make out the end of the tunnel, where the light shone even more brightly. The closer I came to my journey's end the more clearly I could see vague movements which finally crystallised into figures permeated by light. Light-filled figures grazing in meadows of light, climbing trees of light, hunting prey made of light, leaping up hills of light and resting on cliffs of light. Before me stretched a literally paradisal landscape full of golden lakes, silver forests, shining mountains and valleys. And like a Noah's Ark of outsize dimensions and illuminated by billions of floodlights, it was entirely inhabited by animals in angelic form. I knew where I was: in the Eternal Hunting Grounds!

I saw Ambrosius quite close to me – an Ambrosius shining as brightly from within as a defective light bulb just before it explodes. He was sitting on a stack of paper under a tree, busily scribbling with his paw. I called his name, but he simply looked at me without a word and smiled. There stood Alcina, up to her knees in the water of a glittering stream, hooking fish out with her paw and throwing them on the bank. I called her name too, but she was too busy to hear me. All the animals here, whether chimpanzees, polar bears or iguanas, were going about their natural business as they did in real life. But there were no humans getting in the way. There was no more fear in this place, only blessedness and light.

Suddenly I saw movement in the distance, and the blurred outlines of a shape making purposefully in my direction. My gaze followed it, fascinated, for I instinctively felt that its appearance had something to do with my arrival. The figure came closer and closer until I could see it perfectly clearly, and finally it stopped in front of me. It was the spectral apparition of a magnificent white member of our species, shining so brightly that you had to narrow your eyes at the sight of it. The apparition had shining turquoise eyes and a phenomenally full, fluffy coat. He looked at me for a while with an enraptured smile. The other animals didn't seem in any way disturbed by this ghostly figure, but just went on with their former activities perfectly calmly. He probably turned up here at this time every day.

'Welcome, Francis! Had a good journey?' his voice suddenly echoed in my ears. It was a musical voice, a voice full of promise.

'Fabulous, except that the air hostess never once showed up,' I replied. Next moment I asked, 'Is this Heaven?'

'If you like.'

'And are you God?'

'Would you be very disappointed if I said no?'

'No, there are worse things in life.'

'Life?'

'You mean I'm dead? I thought I smelt a rat – if I may make a little in-joke.'

'Do you think you're dead, Francis?'

'Well, last time I saw anything like this was in a whiter-than-white detergent ad on TV.'

'Do you really want to be dead, Francis?'

'Yes,' I said sadly, surprised to find how suddenly my euphoria had worn off. 'To be honest, yes. Where I come from, people with more than two legs aren't as well off as here in this radiant zoo. I'm tired of the sight of suffering. I can't even feel hatred any more; the breath of humanity blights all feelings. And when it strikes an animal the whole species perishes, not just the individual.'

'But what about all those unsolved cases, Francis? What about the harmony and order you were so keen to promote among your kind? Who'll do all that now? Remember your old friend Schopenhauer, who said: "All certainly wish to be delivered from a state of suffering and death, they desire, as the fine phrase has it, to attain eternal bliss and go to heaven, but not on their own two feet. They prefer to be taken there in the natural course of events." Are you going to make things so easy for yourself?'

'To be honest, I haven't stopped to think about it yet. So am I dead now or what?'

'You must answer that question yourself, Francis. This isn't a magical place where your every wish can be read in your eyes. If you want to come in, then come in. First, however, remember that there's still a lot of work waiting for you on earth. But a lot of fulfilment and love too.'

'A lot of work sounds to me like a lot of trouble.'

'Are you used to anything different?'

'No.'

'Then make up your mind. The decision is yours alone, Francis.'

The ability to make decisions was something that had rather failed me since I was shot. The radiant scenery I saw before me was more than tempting: I dared not even speculate about the delicious kinds of food that might be found there, or the dizzying variety of my own kind. All the same, the white apparition's words had given me something to think about. Had I really bidden farewell to our gloomy planet just to escape the struggle like a coward? What had become of my compulsive curiosity? I might have cursed it soundly on many occasions, but secretly I'd always carried it pinned on me like a medal. Wouldn't my dear old grey cells very soon get bored in a land flowing with milk and honey? And the most important question of all: was Gustav to get off so lightly after all the torments I'd been through? Life might not be anything to write home about – but then neither was death.

The shining god of the Felidae slowly began to dematerialise. His questioning glance was still fixed on me, but his kindly countenance was unsteady, rippling as if reflected on the surface of water when you've thrown a pebble in. And not only was the only god I ever met floating away, this whole El Dorado suddenly seemed to be in the process of dissolution. In spite of the brightness, I could still distinguish the outlines of the fabulous landscape and its happy inhabitants quite clearly, but they were slowly overlaid by an even more blinding light, as if someone were trying to burn out the picture and my retinas too.

'The decision is yours alone, Francis,' repeated the celestial philosopher, just before a glaring whiteness blotted everything out and I could see nothing but the light, the light, the light . . .

The light which was shining into one of my eyes, my eyelid being propped open by a finger, was the beam of a torch. A little old man wearing glasses was staring with professional curiosity into my reluctant organ of sight and also, or so it seemed to me, into my inmost being. Then he nodded with mingled surprise and satisfaction and let my eyelid close again. Full of extremely terrestrial pain, I opened my peepers again just a slit and saw the man with the torch leaving the room. The room . . . I knew this room! Good heavens, I knew the whole place! It was none other than Gustav's bedroom, and I was lying curled up on his bed, which smelled as musty as ever. Squinting down at myself I saw that my body was almost entirely wrapped in muslin bandages like an Egyptian mummy. The pain started in the region of my belly, where the bullet had hit me, and then marched in a persistent and purposeful manner straight to my head. However, I was clearly under the influence of some kind of pain-killing drug, so I didn't have to start screeching right away.

I heard voices in the living room. One of them was a woman's voice, but not Francesca's, thank God. I listened for a few minutes, and began to understand what had happened. The woman talking to Gustav in agitated tones was Diana. She was telling him about the environmental programme of reintroducing animals to the wild and its tragic consequences, which hadn't even spared her own pet Ambrosius. Sadly, she told him how in the dark, and in her last desperate desire to shoot the Wild Ones, she had mistaken me for one of them, particularly as the satellite pictures had shown her the whole pack migrating from their forest home. But when she looked more closely at her victim the spirit of the veterinary surgeon she had once been revived in her. She had taken me straight to her house and patched me up in an emergency operation, and in the process she happened to come upon the number tattooed on my rump. That number had led her to Gustav.

Gustav thanked her fervently, his voice shaken at regular intervals by tears of joy. Of course the agonies he was now suffering were the merest pin-pricks compared to what lay ahead. Even in my drugged state, my imagination was working overtime devising various schemes for reprisals. I wondered how long I could spin out my convalescence. Two months, maybe? Four months? Even a whole year? Oh, how I'd hammer home my revulsion, how guilty I'd make him feel! What demands I'd make, what merciless fads and fancies I was going to think up! He'd have to whip cream for me, every day at that, he'd have to buy me fresh lobster straight from the fish market. I'd have it lightly broiled. As for the tap water he usually put in my water bowl, he could tip that down his own throat for all I cared: I was going to insist on nothing but Perrier. And I'd demand a saucer of vanilla ice cream every evening, not just any old variety either, it would have to be Häagen Dazs. If he didn't do as I had every right to require, I'd make a casual movement revealing my scars and look deep and reproachfully into his eyes. That'd do the trick, as sure as I'd set eyes on the Eternal Hunting Grounds!

You may be wondering why I was enthusiastically indulging in revenge fantasies of this nature, when I must surely assume in my present situation that Francesca's nut-cracking project was still poised above my head like a sword of Damocles. The answer is simple. My infallible instincts told me that the problem had solved itself while I was away. At this point in time, of course, I didn't know the precise circumstances. But Gustav was a real old gossip, and the information he felt impelled to impart to visitors who came asking after the invalid over the next few weeks gave me a detailed picture. The sad event had occurred on the night of my flight. Woken by the howling storm, my companion was very worried when he couldn't find me anywhere in the flat. The open bathroom window made him fear the worst, and he tried a hackneyed old ruse. Hoping to lure me back indoors, he made a great deal of noise about opening a fresh tin of food, and in the process he inadvertently spilled half the delicious contents on the floor. Then he went back to bed, but that woke Francesca. She was cross about having her night's rest disturbed, and this time she was the one who couldn't get back to sleep. Feeling an urgent need to relieve herself, she went to the lavatory, and as luck would have it, she trod on the spilt trail of food in the dark. She slipped, fell over and cracked the back of her head on the edge of the toilet bowl. The poor woman died on the spot.

Sad, very sad, but most accidents do occur in the home. To see it as the act of a higher power punishing her wicked designs on a certain species is sheer nonsense, if you ask me, although I must admit that the dispensation-of-providence theory isn't to be dismissed out of hand. I must also admit that I didn't exactly burst into tears when I heard of her bizarre accident. You have to be very careful how you move about in a world ruled by the laws of gravity if you don't happen to be as super-supple as me and my kind. And most of all you want to be even more careful how you tangle with the likes of me, or you may break your own neck and not just other people's hearts. There are some things in heaven and earth to which only my race has access. I will just mention the term psi-trailing.

So I need never have run away at all. But on reflection I came to the conclusion that my flight had been necessary. It introduced me for the first time to those who have to live without a bowl full of food every day. Some of them, like the blind Company of the Merciful, do heroic things for their brothers and sisters in spite of their own sad fate. Whereas others . . . no, I didn't want to keep only those dreadful memories of the Wild Ones alive in my mind. I wanted to dwell on memories of a different kind. For instance, my first meeting with Alcina when she lay there on the heap of leaves like a forest queen, the rays of the sun making her an unreal, radiant being, her pale green eyes narrowed to enchanting slits. I wanted to imagine the members of her tribe finding plenty of prey and the solitude they so desperately needed in the impenetrable forests of Scandinavia. And a few potent males too, to keep the species from dying out. Sometimes inaccurate memories were better than ugly ones. Ambrosius had said, 'One day humans will look at their world and see something strange: an Earth without animals.' What a nightmare notion! I still respected Ambrosius, in spite of what he'd done, but at the same time I sincerely hoped his last words would never come true. I didn't want to live in a lonely world like that, and the funny thing was that humans themselves didn't really want to either.

Gustav, Diana, and the second vet who'd been called in to give me another thorough examination came into the room. I immediately closed my eyes and uttered a pitiful whimpering sound. Thereupon my fat friend began whimpering too, although less from physical pain than from a properly guilty conscience. And quite right too. He bent down, stroked my head carefully with trembling hands, and promised to do all sorts of things to please me if only I'd get better soon. Good Lord above, he even mentioned live mice! I just smiled secretly to myself, thinking: and that's not all you're going to give me, my stupid friend, oh no, that's far from all . . .

And with these rosy prospects in view, the Francis Detective Agency temporarily closes its doors. Should you suspect your wife of straying, or your husband of his forty-third murder, kindly turn to other detectives for now. You may find one quite close to home. But there is one striking feature whereby you can tell real detectives from the inefficient sort: the good ones have sharp claws.

NOTES

1. Of all mammals, cats are world champions at sleeping. They spend about sixteen hours a day in the arms of Morpheus, thus beating even the large and lazy panda, which spends just ten hours of the day asleep. Being switched off for two-thirds of its time, so to speak, a nine-year-old cat has in effect spent only three years awake. However, quantity is not the same thing as quality, so the comfortably laid-back cat cannot relax as thoroughly as its two-legged retainers. Cats do not take their sleep all at once, like humans, but in the short snatches sometimes known as cat-naps. During these naps, which consist of several sleep cycles, their brains are nowhere near as completely 'disconnected' as the human brain. So far as bio-signals are concerned, the cat's deep sleep is more like our own light sleep. And appropriately for a hunter, the cat's 'radar' remains alert even during a siesta. If even a distant mouse-like rustling is heard, the alarm system immediately comes on, and the tiger on stand-by is wide awake at once.

Cats, who often assume the most artistically ornate positions as they doze, can indulge in this lethargic life-style only because they are extremely efficient hunters with few natural enemies. Their natural prey, on the other hand, often consists of creatures who can never sleep for more than a few minutes at a time, such as hares. For obvious reasons, cats are popular 'guinea-pigs' for scientists researching into the nature of sleep, and in that capacity have made heroic contributions to various pioneering discoveries.

2. Some people regard neutering with revulsion, as barbaric butchery and the infringement of a cat's right to develop its personality

freely. They believe that we mutilate our animal companions cruelly to make them easy-care soft toys, and then hypocritically argue that it was a harmless therapeutic measure and all for the pet's own good; sex, we point out, doesn't make you happy. The natural drives of the sanitised Barbie cat cease to be a nuisance to us, and it becomes a toy lion acceptable in polite company.

However, the author can see the arguments on the other side too. Tom cats with their family jewels still functional are genuinely uncontrollable, and in considerable danger of getting severely injured during their constant fights. They also give off a pungent erotic aroma which smells pestilential - to their tin-openers, anyway. Female cats (or queens) who still have all their equipment may easily be 'calling' for a mate the whole time, turning the home upside down with their rampageous behaviour. Too many pregnancies at frequent intervals will leave them suffering from stress, exhaustion, and very likely gynaecological complications too. There is also the constant danger of over-population, since cats breed like the proverbial rabbits. Finally, when you remember that neutered cats live two or three years longer without getting conspicuously overweight, neutering is probably the lesser of two evils in a standard urban household.

3. Cats have an irresistible impulse to sharpen and clean their claws, and will often do it on the sofa or some other treasured piece of furniture. Many cat owners regard this activity as they might the appearance of a nightmare figure from a horror film running amok with a set of knives. However, amputation of a cat's claws for inappropriate scratching is a barbaric mutilation and a peculiarly cruel kind of torture. For one thing, the cat uses its claws in the daily task of grooming, for combing and cleaning the fur, and cannot do without them. Anyone who has ever been unable to scratch in order to relieve an itch will understand the gravity of the situation. Moreover, de-clawed cats cannot get a proper grip when they try to climb in instinctive response to another animal need, and if they are in flight from a dog (or another and hostile cat) the consequences can be fatal. If an ill-disposed neighbour goes for it with malicious intent, a cat deprived

of its sharp daggers cannot defend itself properly. And finally, cats whose claws have been amputated are unable to hunt and so cannot fend for themselves in an emergency.

Amputation of the claws, also euphemistically known by the ancient Greek term 'onyxectonomy', is illegal in many European countries. In the leading international cat breeding associations it is condemned even more strongly than doping in the Olympic Games. You should do everything possible in the way of conditioning to divert your cat's urges to an official scratching post. At the first sign that your pet vandal has his beady eye on the furniture, take him to the spot where scratching is allowed. If in doubt, it is really better not to keep a cat at all if you cannot live with its claws as well as its velvet paws.

4. With mysterious regularity, cats will often say goodbye to the four walls of home and go on their travels with some unknown end in view. It is as mysterious an exodus as the strange disappearance of a husband who pops out for cigarettes and vanishes into some twilight zone never to be seen again. Humans were puzzling over this behaviour pattern even in ancient times; superstition says that the departure of a cat means someone in a house is going to die. There is an old Flemish proverb, 'When the cat goes out, death comes in.' Today, however, more rational explanations are sought. Perhaps the sensitive runaway is simply responding 'allergically' to some subtle change in its familiar surroundings and urgently requires a change of scene. Or then again, perhaps the cat has received Zen enlightenment during its meditative trance beside the radiator and is following in the steps of Siddhartha to turn the wheel of Karma. Or of course there is the remote possibility that E.T. and the rest of the UFO brigade are regularly stealing cats for vivisection with a view to solving the cosmic mystery of self-satisfaction.

5. The Chartreux (sometimes called the Chartreuse), a French breed extremely similar to the British Blue, is a handsome, muscular animal with a broad head and well-proportioned short legs, about the closest a cat comes to being a teddy bear. With its yellow

or golden eyes and its short, thick, velvety fur, grey to blue-grey in colour, this cuddly creature captures small children's hearts. The Chartreux may appear calm and lethargic, but it can be a tiger in sheep's clothing, and in emergency will show its pugnacious, battling nature.

There is a widespread idea that the monks of La Grande Chartreuse monastery in France bred these cats in the Middle Ages to rid themselves of mice. According to this story the good clerics, who also made a commercial hit with their famous green liqueur, raised their new breed from related cats imported from South Africa. Unfortunately closer examination shows that the legend is only an old wives' tale. According to the Prior of La Grande Chartreuse, no sister house ever existed in South Africa, nor did any Carthusian monks ever bring back African cats. The theory that the cat takes its name from the simple grey robes allegedly worn by Carthusian monks also belongs in the realm of fantasy, since the Carthusians have always worn pure white habits. More probably the name goes back to a kind of wool widely known in France in the past. Finally, the fact that no written records whatever about any kind of cat-breeding experiments exist at La Grande Chartreuse casts further doubt on the legend.

However, those culinary experts the French did add to the history of the Chartreux cat, if not very creditably. According to Linnaeus, these cats used to be fattened, killed and eaten, for instance stuffed and roasted; this gruesome dish even found its way into old German menus as 'Dachshund'. Furriers cured the coat and sold it as 'petit gris'; the finished product, trimmed and dyed, was sold to gullible consumers as otter skin.

The famous natural scientists Linnaeus and Buffon recognised the Chartreux cat as a separate breed, and in the 1930s a French veterinary surgeon gave it a scientific name of its own: *Felis catus cartusianorum*. Our oldest documented record of a blue-grey cat dates from 1558 and comes from Rome: a poet sadly laments the death of his little pet.

6. When the cat lies lazily in the sun licking itself it is not just cooling itself off (through evaporation) and getting clean. Using

elements already present in the body, ultra-violet rays produce an essential elixir of life in the fur: this is vitamin D, the sunlight or anti-rickets vitamin. The cat supplements its normal diet with this extract, which enables it to store calcium and phosphate in its bones. Calcium, the silver-grey alkaline earth metal, gives the teeth their biting power and the bones their strength. Rickets, a severe form of bone softening in children, was known on the continent of Europe in the past as the English disease; the idea was that the prevalence of fog in the British Isles kept the invigorating rays of the sun away. Children affected by rickets were a pitiful sight, pigeon-breasted and with severely deformed skeletons.

Rickets in the strict sense seldom occurs in cats, but similar conditions have been found in kittens with inadequate calcium or vitamin D in their diet. The condition deprives the cat of vitality and causes fragile, deformed or fractured bones. Vitamin D is present in milk, fish products and tinned cat-food. It is particularly important to make sure that housebound cats who seldom or never see 'real' daylight out of doors get an adequate supply. Paradoxically, however, too much vitamin D can be harmful, causing symptoms similar to a lack of it.

7. It is one of the persistent and proverbial myths about the animal kingdom that hostility must inevitably exist between dogs and cats because 'language barriers' and their irreconcilably different characters preclude peaceful coexistence on the part of the two arch-enemies. In nature - and therefore in their genetic information - there is no provision for cats and dogs to meet, since they occupy different ecological niches and hunt different prey. Temperamentally, dog and cat are indeed opposites. At a first encounter the cat will remain cool and reserved, sounding out the situation as befits a loner. The dog, on the other hand, with its extrovert pack-animal nature, will immediately makes a boisterous attempt at rapprochement. The cat misinterprets this boisterous approach as a hostile infringement of its own personal space (or 'flight distance'). Many further misunderstandings can easily arise because non-verbal messages mean different things in dog and cat language. Cats, decorous creatures that they are, touch

noses with each other as a greeting. The dog observes no such niceties, but puts his nose straight up to the cat's tail to sniff it - from the cat's point of view, a serious breach of good manners. The cat will raise a paw in warning, making the dog even more bumptious, since among dogs a raised paw is a friendly gesture. The dog gets the wrong message from the agitated twitching of a cat's tail, because his own kind wag their tails when they are feeling friendly and relaxed. If the cat eventually turns and runs because (as we all know) the cleverer gives way first, it is only giving the dog the fatal signal to act as a hound and start the chase. In a direct frontal attack from a cat, however, the dog will usually be the loser, because cats have faster reactions and because a prey animal which turns to attack simply does not fit into the canine scheme of things. Cats are just as surprised if an aggressive rat ventures to attack.

In spite of such handicaps, the two hostile powers can easily come to tolerate each other and even strike up firm friendships. Out of over five million dogs in German households, almost half live with other domestic pets, a great many of them with cats. Fraternisation works best, of course, if the two 'enemies' come into the house as young animals and grow up together. In those circumstances even cats and mice can become good friends.

An affectionate female gorilla called Koko recently attracted much attention by making a pet of a cat; when her pet died as a result of an accident Koko grieved until she was given another cat.

Murr the cat, the amusing protagonist in a novel by the Romantic author E.T.A. Hoffmann, makes friends with a poodle called Ponto in his youth. In the course of the novel Murr even writes a learned treatise of his own (entitled 'Thought and Instinct, or Cat and Dog'), proving among other things that 'words' used by the two species (e.g. the dog's 'bow-wow' and the cat's 'miaow') have the same etymological origin.

This is not really so fantastic a notion, for many million years ago dog and cat were indeed closely related, both belonging to a super-family of dog-like and cat-like carnivores. Recently a French clergyman and his family moved to a new parish some two hundred kilometres away. They took their German Shepherd dog with them but left their cat in their old home. Two weeks after the move the dog disappeared – and came back to his new home seven weeks later with the cat in tow.

8. There is probably no other beast of prey in the wild so misunderstood, as a result of ignorance and direct horror propaganda, as the European wildcat (*Felis silvestris*). The wild cousin of our domestic cat is noticeably larger and sturdier and can weigh up to thirteen kilograms. The wildcat has shorter legs, smaller ears and a more sloping forehead than the domestic cat, as well as a thick ringed tail. At first glance, its coat pattern suggests a grey tabby domestic cat, but the blurred black striped pattern of the wildcats' fur is in fact unique to them.

Felis silvestris lives in thickly overgrown woodland areas, and will also make itself a nest in cracks in the rock or hollow trees. It is a timid loner, impossible to approach, and leads a largely solitary life, coming together with other members of its species only for a few weeks in spring in order to mate. After mating, the female wildcat has two to four kittens, which are blind at birth. These kittens cannot be kept as domestic pets; sooner or later, however sweet and playful they seem, they will change and become ferocious. Wildcats occupy an important ecological niche, keeping mice and other harmful vermin in check.

The wildcat lived in Central European forests for over three hundred thousand years, but it has been systematically decimated in the last few centuries. In the British Isles it now survives only in Scotland. In modern Germany, the setting of this novel, there are only about fourteen hundred wild cats. Continental hunters deliberately spread disinformation to the effect that wildcats attacked hares, fawns and other of their own favourite prey. The 'grey ghost' was even said to be in touch with the powers of darkness and able to kill a grown man. For superstitious reasons, most hunters would 'bless' their guns with holy water before going after wildcats. Many experts believe that the systematic reintroduction of *Felis silvestris* to various parts of Europe can at most only delay the extinction of the species.

9. Although our tame domestic cats were probably created by breeding from their African ancestors, they can interbreed successfully with the European wildcat. As things stand, the domestic cat can even produce offspring by the North American lynx. Finally, there is even a possibility that there are no limits at all to mating between small cats (of the genus *Felis*). According to the textbooks, the cross-breeding of wild and domestic cats ought to produce infertile hybrids, but some of these bastard cats have obviously retained the ability to reproduce. There are some strange hybrids in the depths of northern European forests, and it would be surprising if the domestic cat did not have a few drops of wild European blood in its veins. That transfusion very probably occurred in the ancient forests of European folklore; it cannot yet be proved for certain, but at some point new forensic techniques such as genetic fingerprinting will give us a definite answer. So far as today's domestic cat is concerned, a fling with a wildcat can take a nasty turn; foresters have seen such wildcats turn to scratching furies at the sight of a decadent domestic pet.

10. The belief that cats have an amazing and indeed paranormal ability to find their way home is so deeply rooted that it periodically surfaces in the media, embroidered with ever new episodes. Almost every week you can hear of some Puss in Boots who accidentally fetches up in a strange and distant place but finds his way home with dreamlike certainty. Americans, with their taste for the road movie, have versions in which the trip is country-wide, from coast to coast. Examined closely, the tale has two different variants which should be distinguished from each other. The conventional variety, whereby the cat finds its way home from some strange place, can be explained in principle without calling on any psi factor. The cat may have an acoustic picture of the sounds of home at the back of its head, and finds its way by that map. Or it may take a fix from the position of the sun, as travellers in former times used to. Perhaps cats, like whales, may even have a magnetic sense which allows them to navigate as if by a compass.

However, there are cases suggesting some paranormal force at work, stories in which a cat has been left behind but follows its master long distances to a new and hitherto entirely unknown home. This variant cannot be explained by even the most remarkable achievements of the senses, and is often called psi-trailing and regarded as an extra-sensory talent. Some decades ago the American parapsychologist J.B. Rhine collected and analysed all documented cases. The biggest sensation was a cat belonging to a New York veterinary surgeon who moved from New York to California. Several months later the cat, who had been left behind in New York, turned up energetically demanding entry to his new home and made straight for his favourite place in a comfortable armchair.

We can make what we like of such mysterious journeys. Desmond Morris, the British cat expert, thinks it is pointless and leads nowhere to look for parapsychological explanations of the marvels and mysteries of nature, thus stifling the curiosity of the inquiring mind. Ever since the times of the Ancient Egyptians, however, the cat has presented mankind with mysteries which are peculiar to itself and will put the abilities of any two-legged medium in the shade.

11. Although the eyes of the cat are among the greatest masterpieces created by the 'Blind Watchmaker' - evolution - those amazing organs are not much good at perceiving colour. As with primates (including humans), they face forward, and display their aesthetic beauty in some of mankind's oldest painted records. They are very large in relation to skull size and therefore absorb a great deal of light. In addition, the back of the eye is covered by the reflective tapetum, which throws back the 'used' rays of light. This amplifier of the residual light makes the cat's reflective eyes powerful tools for night vision, and military commanders have tried to make use of them in nocturnal warfare.

The light-sensitive layer of the eyes, the retina, consists of two kinds of photocells, rods and cones. The rods, which are far more numerous than the cones, react very sensitively to differences between light and dark, and are situated mainly in the outer area of the retina. The cones, responsible for colour perception and close-up vision, function only in daylight and are concentrated in the centre of the retina, in humans a circular pit or fovea. The feline fovea, containing only a few cones, is a horizontal line. Cats thus have very sharp eyes for spotting mice who happen to wander across their field of vision, but it would be hard for them to see the letters of newsprint properly, and they have difficulty in adjusting their lenses to the macro-area which shows close-up detail. Cats are therefore sometimes disorientated if the object of their interest is right in front of their faces.

Because of the small number of colour cones in cats' eyes, it was thought for a long time that they could see the world only in black and white. However, it was then shown that they can be trained, rather laboriously, to distinguish between certain primary colours. In time they can tell red, blue and white apart. On the whole, however, colour is not very important to them: all mice are grey at night anyway. But American zoologists have recently discovered that the domestic cat has a latent ability to see in colour at birth. The Spanish wildcat, which like many other archaic relations of our domestic cat hunts its prey in the bright midday sun, has about twice as many cones in its pupil and is thus fully able to perceive colour. When it is born the domestic cat, whose forebears at some point took to seeking food by night near human settlements, has just the same kind of colour-perceptive fovea. The ability to see colour, however, is soon eradicated by genetic programming. Probably this ghost of an ability in the cat's eye still exists only because it could be useful at some point if the cat were ever to revert to its old life-style.